A Medieval Treasury

An Exhibition of Medieval Art
from the Third to the Sixteenth Century

ROBERT G. CALKINS

4354

ANDREW DICKSON WHITE MUSEUM OF ART, CORNELL UNIVERSITY, ITHACA, NEW YORK

OCTOBER 8–NOVEMBER 3, 1968

MUNSON-WILLIAMS-PROCTOR INSTITUTE, UTICA, NEW YORK

NOVEMBER 10–DECEMBER 8, 1968

Cover illustration:
No. 40. Crozier Head
St. Michael Killing the Dragon
French, Limoges, 2nd quarter 13th Century

Preface

A Medieval Treasury brings to Central New York for the first time a comprehensive presentation of the art of the Middle Ages. Encouraged by their successful cosponsorship two years ago of the exhibition Japanese Painters of the Floating World, the Andrew Dickson White Museum of Art at Cornell University in Ithaca and the Munson-Williams-Proctor Institute in Utica have cooperated closely in this new venture.

For two smaller American museums to attempt a substantial exhibition of medieval art from American collections is ambitious, to say the least. Although there are great treasures among the medieval holdings of American museums and collectors, most are on permanent display, and many others are in extremely fragile condition. It is, therefore, a tribute to the scholarship and the dedication of the exhibition's director, Professor Robert G. Calkins of Cornell University, that such a distinguished treasury of medieval objects has been assembled. He has organized every phase of this exhibition from its inception, and the exhibiting institutions are deeply indebted to him.

We should also like to express our appreciation to the museums, galleries, and collectors who have kindly allowed us to borrow their treasures. The standard of quality maintained in the exhibition is the most tangible evidence of their enthusiasm and generosity. In addition, on behalf of both institutions and all those who enjoy A Medieval Treasury, we should like to thank the New York State Council on the Arts for its assistance in making possible the publication of this catalogue.

THOMAS W. LEAVITT,
Director, White Museum of Art,
Cornell University

EDWARD H. DWIGHT,
Director, Museum of Art,
Munson-Williams-Proctor Institute

Lenders to the Exhibition

The William Hayes Ackland Memorial Art Center, University of North
  Carolina, Chapel Hill
Albright-Knox Art Gallery, Buffalo
Allen Memorial Art Museum, Oberlin College, Oberlin, Ohio
The Art Museum, Princeton University, Princeton, New Jersey
Cincinnati Art Museum, Cincinnati
City Art Museum of St. Louis, St. Louis
The Cleveland Museum of Art, Cleveland
Cornell University Library, Department of Rare Books, Cornell University,
  Ithaca, New York
The Denver Art Museum, Denver
The Detroit Institute of Arts, Detroit
Paul Drey Gallery, New York City
Duke University, Durham, North Carolina
Fogg Art Museum, Harvard University, Cambridge, Massachusetts
Michael Hall Fine Arts, Inc., New York City
Lansburgh–Colorado College Collection, Colorado Springs, Colorado
The Metropolitan Museum of Art, New York City
The Pierpont Morgan Library, New York City
Museum of Art, Rhode Island School of Design, Providence
Museum of Fine Arts, Boston
The Newark Museum, Newark, New Jersey
Philadelphia Museum of Art, Philadelphia
Mr. Francis Waring Robinson, Detroit
Professor and Mrs. Rudolph B. Schlesinger, Ithaca, New York
Seattle Art Museum, Seattle
University of Kansas Museum of Art, Lawrence
Wadsworth Atheneum, Hartford, Connecticut
The Walters Art Gallery, Baltimore
Wellesley College Art Museum, Wellesley, Massachusetts
Worcester Art Museum, Worcester, Massachusetts
M. H. De Young Memorial Museum, San Francisco

Table of Contents

v

Foreword

The present exhibition of medieval treasures coincides with and reflects the heightened interest in medieval art, which has been generated by a number of large and very important exhibitions both in the United States and abroad. The spectacular display entitled Treasures from Medieval France held in Cleveland in the winter of 1966–1967 and the comprehensive exhibition of European Gothic art from the twelfth to the fourteenth century held in Paris in the spring of 1968 are to be followed by an important show of medieval art from private collections at the Cloisters from October 1968 to January 1969, one of Romanesque sculpture at the Rhode Island School of Design in the spring of 1969, and a major show on the sources of the Gothic at the Metropolitan Museum and the Cloisters in 1970.

For our purpose it did not seem appropriate to concentrate on medieval art from a particular nationality, source, or period. Preferably, this first presentation in the Finger Lakes area of material from the Middle Ages should strive to make available a broader picture of the era. Embracing diverse examples dating from the third to the sixteenth century, the exhibition endeavors to bring to the Ithaca and Utica communities a glimpse of the full and varied panorama of secular and religious art in the Middle Ages. In addition, the exhibition has been designed to provide a useful, and hopefully provocative, body of material for students in the area who are studying the history of medieval art and for those who are participating in Cornell's Graduate Medieval Studies program. To the best of our knowledge, in the last twenty-eight years only two major exhibitions of a comprehensive nature covering the entire medieval period and drawing on the rich resources of American museums have been held—the Arts of the Middle Ages, 1000–1400, at Boston in 1940 and Medieval Art at Tulsa, Oklahoma, in 1965. We therefore sought to provide a sampling from American collections, with a strong emphasis on the holdings of other university or college museums and galleries.

It was decided to organize the exhibition around a corpus of smaller medieval objects, metal work, ivory carvings, and illuminated manuscripts, those which make up, in Hanns Swarzenski's appropriate phrase, "the art of the Church Treasures." To this core were added secular objects, larger representative pieces of sculpture, two panels of stained glass, some early textiles, and a tapestry. Panel paintings were not considered; they are prone to the damaging effects of temperature and humidity changes encountered in being moved from one place to another. Even in the chosen categories, because of the rarity, fragility, and value of most things medieval, many objects could not, understandably, be made available. Yet the generosity and enthusiasm of the lenders for this project have made it possible to assemble a representative selection of most of the important phases of medieval art from Western Europe. Most regrettable is the lack of any object of Carolingian art; representative examples from this era are extremely rare in this country and are so delicate and precious as to preclude travel. But a glimmer of at least one aspect of Carolingian art may be seen in the Corvey Gospels fragment, the single superb example of early Ottonian art which we were able to obtain. For the other broad periods which fall within the Middle Ages—Early Christian, Byzantine, Merovingian, Romanesque, and Gothic— it is hoped that we have opened the eyes of the viewer to the splendor of the different materials, to the marvelous variety of objects, to the evolving changes of style, to the complexities of meaning, and even to some of the art-historical problems which exist within the realm of medieval art.

In the Introduction, an attempt will be made to explain more fully the significance of the kinds of artifacts exhibited and how they relate to the general tenor of the times. Detailed information concerning each of the objects will be found in the Catalogue, and for the interested student a complete bibliography of references cited may be found at the end of the volume. The plates and catalogue entries generally follow in chronological order, although within specific periods, types of objects are kept together (Romanesque manuscripts, for example, or Gothic ivories) to give a better sense of development within a particular craft.

It is simply not possible to give recognition here to all the many persons who have assisted in a variety of ways in the preparation of this exhibition and to whom we are deeply grateful. Special acknowledgement should go to Professor Martie W. Young, Chairman of the Department of History of Art at Cornell, who first proposed the idea of this show and who gave continual encouragement throughout the undertaking. My sincere thanks are due to the following persons who responded to the project in its early stages with enthusiasm and generosity and therefore made it possible: Miss Frances Jones, The Art Museum, Princeton University; Professor Donald Eddy, Department of Rare Books, Cornell University Library; Mr. Francis W. Robinson, Detroit Institute of Arts; Miss Carmen Gomez-Moreno and Mr. William Forsyth, Metropolitan Museum of Art; Mr. Michael Hall; Mr. Mark Lansburgh, Colorado College, Colorado Springs; Mr. John Plummer, the Pierpont Morgan Library; Mr. David DuBon, Philadelphia Museum of Art; Miss Louisa Dresser, Worcester Art Museum; Mr. Richard H. Randall Jr. and Miss Dorothy Miner, the Walters Art Gallery, Baltimore. Mr. John Beckwith of the Victoria and Albert Museum, London, and Madame Gh.

Derveaux, Musées Royaux d'Art et d'Histoire, Brussels, spared their valuable time to give me important information and insights into the problems posed by some of the objects.

I also wish to thank Mrs. Katrina Morse, Registrar, the White Art Museum, who tended to the myriad of administrative details, Mrs. Joan Udovitch who served valiantly as a Research Assistant, the staff of the Research Department of the Cornell University Library, who coped with a never-ending deluge of requests for material, and to Mr. Donald Feint, Gallery Superintendent, the Andrew Dickson White Museum of Art, who handled the difficult problems of installation at Cornell. It is with a deep sense of gratitude that I also acknowledge the efforts of my wife, Ann, who helped with revisions of the text, of Mrs. Carol O'Brien, who typed the manuscript, of Mr. Kelvin Arden and Mr. Franklin Hurtt, who designed the catalogue, and of the staff of the Office of University Publications, who prepared the manuscript for publication. Finally, I wish to express my sincere appreciation to the Humanities Faculty Research Grants Committee of Cornell University for their award of a grant which supported the research for this project.

Robert G. Calkins

Ithaca, New York
August 1968

A Medieval Treasury

As so often happens when historical periods are categorized, the term "Middle Ages" is both misleading and deprecatory. It derives from the Renaissance view of history and culture, articulated by Petrarch when he branded the literature and thought of the period between the fall of Rome and the revival of learning in his own time (1304–1374) as ugly and barbaric manifestations of a "Dark" age.[1] This view was perpetuated by Italian humanists and chroniclers in the fifteenth and sixteenth centuries, who wrote that the liberal arts of the ancients, "which were almost extinct," were revived in their own time.[2] They dismissed the contributions of the medieval period to the later development of western man. They forgot that medieval men saw themselves as direct heirs of antiquity who sought to maintain the continuity of their institutions with those of Rome by turning to classical times for inspiration, and ignored the fact that it was precisely the medieval scriptoria and institutions of learning, the monasteries and universities, which preserved most of the antique texts during the period of their "neglect."

Of all the historical periods, the Middle Ages is one of the most varied and imprecise. Generally, it can be considered to begin with the recognition of Christianity as the state religion of Rome in the early fourth century, though an approximate date of A.D. 500, concurrent with the complete dissolution of the Roman Empire, is frequently cited. Certainly the political, social, and economic institutions of the Early Christian period, at least through the fourth century, remain Late Roman, and the art of this era remains Late Antique. Yet the developments after 500 cannot be fully understood without reference to this time of transition. At the other end of the period, medieval attitudes and institutions blend into those of the Renaissance, perhaps as early as the fourteenth century and certainly by the end of the first third of the fifteenth century in Italy, but not until the mid-fifteenth or even early sixteenth century in northern Europe. Between the almost imperceptible commencement and gradual denouement of the Middle Ages, we have over

[1] *De sui ipsius et multarum ignorantia;* see Theodore Mommsen's discussion in "Petrarch's Conception of the Dark Ages," *Speculum,* XVII (1942), 226–242.

[2] Marsilo Ficino in a letter to Paul of Middleburg, 1492, quoted in Peter Murray and Linda Murray, *The Art of the Renaissance* (New York, 1963), p. 7.

a millennium, twelve hundred kaleidoscopic years of institutions and periods.

The one constant factor throughout these centuries was the common center around which all life was organized, the Christian Church. As the peoples of Europe became Christianized—and this process was still going on in the ninth century under the Carolingian Empire—they embraced a spiritual force which dominated every facet of their lives, an ecclesiastical hierarchy that shaped the course of political events and determined the structure of society. It is for this reason that the term "medieval" applies best to those regions of Europe and to the countries around the Mediterranean, including the Byzantine Empire, that were Christian.

At the same time, the climate of medieval Europe was also determined by threats from without. There were waves of barbarian invasions and constant attacks from the Norsemen. There was the ever-present danger from Islam, which emerged as a powerful adversary, half invading Europe by the middle of the eighth century and still giving cause for grave insecurity in the fifteenth. All these served to mold the Christian faith, which began passively, into the Church Militant. The militant posture of the church, culminating in the Crusades sent to free the Holy Land from the infidel, was a direct consequence of the antagonism of the two faiths, ostensibly on a spiritual level, in practice on a temporal level in the acquisition and retention of territory.

THE MIDDLE AGES AND MEDIEVAL ART

Medieval art must be seen against the background of ecclesiastical domination, the evolution of a feudal society, and the slow re-emergence of cities and a mercantile economy. The art produced in the first centuries of the Christian era was so thoroughly rooted in the traditions and style of Late Roman art that there is barely any noticeable transformation in outward form after Constantine (No. 3) declared Christianity the state religion. For a long time, Christianity and the pagan Roman religions existed side by side, and characteristically Roman types of representations were for the most part merely transformed into Christian images by the addition of specifically Christian symbols. The Late Antique manner of treating the still idealized human body is manifested in the early ivory of Dionysus (No. 1). A contemporary ivory depicting a carpenter (No. 2) reveals a continuation of Roman illusionism in a scene that might be pagan, Christian, or merely genre. Both were created at a moment when the hold of Christianity on the people of the Roman Empire was steadily increasing. These two reliefs are more closely allied with the traditional art of Rome; the specific contributions of the Christians at this time seem to be somewhat limited. During the periods of persecution, cryptic symbols such as that of the fish and the anchor appeared in the catacombs and on funerary monuments. In the exhibited example (No. 8), the fish in the form of a dolphin borrows directly from a favorite pagan symbol. Early representations of Christ were also based on pagan prototypes, and whether He is depicted in the guise of a lawgiver, a philosopher, or a Good Shepherd (No. 4), His youthful and idealized countenance reflects the traditional forms of the youthful Apollo or even of Orpheus. In Egypt, where a local offshoot of the Christian religion, the Coptic church, sprang up in the fourth century, similar evidence of pagan forms and bucolic themes may be observed in surviving decorative textiles (Nos. 9 and 10), while symbols appropriate to both native Egyptian cults and Christianity appear in a number of reliefs believed to date from this confused period of merging beliefs (No. 5).

In the disturbed period that followed the total dissolution of the Roman Empire in Europe, wandering barbarian tribes swept across Germany and France and into Italy and Spain. They brought with them another tradition, far removed from the classical heritage of the Mediterranean countries, which made a strong impact on the type and form of art produced. From the social and economic point of view, this migration period was really the "Dark Ages"; from the artistic point of view, the nomadic and warlike character of the tribes for the most part precluded the creation of monumental forms of art.[3] Most of the artistic remains of these tribes are small portable ornaments for personal attire—fibulae, belt buckles (Nos. 20–22), trappings for armament such as sword hilts and shield decorations, and ornamental utensils. The majority of these objects followed their owners to the grave, and some may even have been created especially for inclusion among the buried treasure of important chieftains. The decoration employed on these artifacts demonstrates the primitive penchant for highly intricate and sophisticated geometric and zoomorphic forms. There is a sense of the primeval, menacing aspect of nature in the twisting, biting snakes and birds, as well as a quality of magic in the ordered, yet purposefully obscured, geometric frets, meanders, spirals, and interlaces.

So strong was the decorative appeal of these so-called barbarian forms that we find them intruding upon and becoming integrated with the art forms of a more Christian and classical heritage throughout the pre-Romanesque and Romanesque periods. One of the most spectacular fusions of both traditions is exemplified by the Lindisfarne Gospels in the British Museum, produced in Northumbria about 800. Almost two centuries later, many of the same devices were still being employed in late Carolingian and early Ottonian illumination (No. 23). Although the actual forms became transformed, some of the ferociousness underlying much of barbarian art continues to manifest itself in the inhabited foliage of decorative initials (Nos. 25–28) and carved capitals (No. 49) of the eleventh and twelfth centuries.

Under Charlemagne, art not only served the Church but also the state. With the establishment of the Holy Roman Empire in 800, every conceivable device was employed to further a self-conscious, deliberate revival of Late

[3] Excellent historical surveys of this period are to be found in J. M. Wallace-Hadrill, *The Barbarian West: The Early Middle Ages, A.D. 400–1000* (2nd rev. ed., New York, 1962), and in Philippe Verdier's summary in Marvin C. Ross, *Arts of the Migration Period in the Walters Art Gallery* (Baltimore, 1961), pp. 121–171.

Antique political institutions that would make the new Roman Empire seem like a continuation of the old. To this end, scholars were imported into court circles; classical grammars and treatises were assiduously copied in the newly founded scriptoria; the Palatine complex at Aachen was modeled after the Lateran Palace in Rome; and Charlemagne was seen as a direct heir of the first Christian emperor, Constantine. Artisans under imperial patronage turned back to Early Christian and Late Antique models, infusing the art of the North with a new classicism that served to give the *renovatio* a visual form. Something of the mixture of classical forms and inherent northern traditions may be seen in the later Corvey Gospels (No. 23), where the purple-dyed vellum, epigraphic capitals, and palmette decoration in the Late Roman imperial manner coexist with zoomorphic forms, interlaces, and confused decorative monograms of letters derived from barbarian metalwork and pre-Carolingian manuscript illumination.

After the break-up of the Carolingian empire, a new period of barbarian invasions set in; Norsemen, Hungarians, and Saracens beset Europe on all sides. A modicum of stability was restored in the late tenth century by the Salian emperors, who revived the Holy Roman Empire on German lands. This new "Ottonian Empire," named after the Ottos who were the first ruling members of the dynasty, survived until the latter half of the eleventh century. Art again became a subject of imperial and ecclesiastical patronage, but the sources of inspiration were now slightly different. In addition to Late Antique, Carolingian forms were emulated in an effort to give a sense of continuity to the visual manifestations of the Holy Roman Empire. At the same time, in a deliberate attempt to elevate the status of the Latin Western Empire to a level commensurate with that of the Byzantine Eastern Empire, Otto II married the Byzantine Princess Theophano. As a result, Byzantine artifacts, and no doubt artisans, were imported into the German realm. The particular character of Ottonian art, a consequence of the fusion of various reinterpretations of Antique, Carolingian, and Byzantine elements, reflects the immediate concerns of contemporary political and religious life. Though the present exhibition contains nothing that manifests the more significant aspects of sculpture or manuscript illumination of the Ottonian period, the Corvey Gospels (No. 23), which are actually of early Ottonian origin, do in fact continue aspects of Carolingian illumination and introduce eastern, Sassanian-Byzantine elements into the textilelike designs of its frontispiece.

Something of the hieratic and iconic severity and otherworldliness of Byzantine art which made a great impact on the art of the Ottonian and Romanesque periods in Europe may be seen in the few ivories, manuscript illuminations, and enamel plaques presented here. Although we cannot show the shimmering mosaics of Daphne and Hosias Lucas, the resplendent enamels and miniatures strive for similar contrasts of translucent color against glittering gold (Nos. 16–17) and reflect analogous narrative techniques (No. 18) and inherent classical treatments of form (No. 19). As late as the mid-thirteenth century in southern Italy, the miniature of the *Majestas Domini*

(No. 30) from the Conradin Bible achieves the same breadth and monumental presence, commensurate with its scale, as the Pantocrator of the Italo-Byzantine mosaics in the cathedrals of Palermo and Monreale.

During the eleventh and twelfth centuries, the period normally called "Romanesque" because the architecture and sculpture were considered to be *in more Romano*,[4] we are confronted with a diversity of styles and a variety of momentous changes. It was an age of unbounded new activity in building. In a famous letter written shortly after the year 1000, the Cluniac monk Raoul Glaber noted that "it was as if the whole earth, having cast off the old by shaking itself, were clothing itself everywhere in the white robe of the church."[5] The era was thus one of consolidation and expansion of the monastic orders, with Cluny becoming the most powerful in all of Europe in the early twelfth century. It was an era in which the faithful undertook long, arduous pilgrimages to the tomb of St. James the Major, the only apostle buried on European soil, at Santiago de Compostela in Spain (No. 53), or to Rome and to the shrine of St. Michael at Monte Gargano (Monte Sant'Angelo) in Italy, or to the Holy Land itself. It was an era in which the almost obsessive veneration of saints' relics, and the proliferation of the relics themselves, created a demand for countless precious reliquaries of gold and enamel (Nos. 34–35). Concurrently, an entirely new solution to the church plan, with a long nave and chapels placed around the apse, was designed to handle the throngs of pilgrims worshiping at many shrines. The massive, heavy, barrel-vaulted structures visually transformed the Church into a Citadel of Heaven. At the same time, the Church became militant at the end of the eleventh century, taking up the sword against Islam to drive the infidel from the Holy Land in the First Crusade.

A proud stance and militant purpose is evident in the powerfully juxtaposed volumes of Romanesque churches with their resolute accumulation of forms mounting in measured and inevitable cadence through apsidal chapels, ambulatory, apse, and transept to the crossing tower. A sense of architectonic purpose may be discerned in a few of the present examples of Romanesque sculpture. The bold relief figure of St. Peter (No. 54) conforms to its stone block. Two romanesque capitals (Nos. 49–50) state their basic volumes, forming transitions from the cylindrical columns to the rectangular load-bearing areas on top. The decorative scheme conforms to and visually assists the supportive function. Nowhere is the fusion of sculptural and architectural statement more emphatically stated than in the figured column from Santiago de Compostela (No. 53), where sculpture serves an architec-

[4] See John Beckwith, *Early Medieval Art* (New York and London, 1964), pp. 166–169, for an excellent discussion of the pitfalls of the commonly accepted term "Romanesque." It should be noted, however, that Beckwith's solution, that of considering the art of the period as a "diffusion and development" of imperial art, poses as many problems as the old, misleading, but convenient label.

[5] Quoted in Elizabeth G. Holt, *A Documentary History of Art*, Vol. I: *The Middle Ages and Renaissance* (New York, 1957), p. 18. (Henceforth "Holt, 1957"; short titles consisting of author and date will be used for works already cited.)

tural function and an architectural element becomes sculpture. With this statement begins the genesis of the Gothic, a development which leads to the jamb figures at Chartres and eventually to a complete detachment of sculpture from the architectural fabric. In contrast, the Italian tradition of placing relief plaques (No. 48) against a planar facade retains a more classical, friezelike aspect that is essentially unarchitectural, juxtaposing sculpture and architecture rather than fusing them.

In the same way that monumental sculpture tended to act in concert with architecture, many images of the faith reflected the sternness of dogma and the evangelical zeal of the period. Cult images of the Virgin showed the Mother of God crowned and unapproachable and the infant already conducting the Final Adjudication (No. 56); monumental tympanums over the portals of churches showed Christ in the apocalyptic vision surrounded by the symbolic beasts of the Evangelists accompanied either by the four and twenty elders (No. 52) or by elaborately worked-out Last Judgment scenes. The fearful vision over the portals of these churches was but a prelude to the visual lessons to be learned inside, where capitals related the incidents of the Bible (No. 50) and made clear the rewards of virtues and the punishments of vices.

But not all Romanesque art was severe and didactic. Bibles and religious tracts were filled with illuminated initials in which all manner of contorted beasts writhed and bit each other and in which men climbed through curling vines and fought with daemonic monsters (Nos. 26–28). This same vivacious and sometimes irreverent trend was reflected in the sculpted capitals of churches and cloisters (No. 49), occurring frequently alongside those depicting incidents from the Bible. Equally fanciful were similar inhabited scrolls employed in metalwork, as in candlesticks (No. 47) and in the supports for crosses (No. 43). Perhaps a legacy of earlier barbarian ornament, these foliate forms inhabited by exotic beasts permitted artisans to display the full range of their imagination and skill.[6] So prevalent and arresting did these forms become that Bernard of Clairvaux singled them out in a justly famous passage in his criticism of the excesses of the Cluniac order:

But in the cloister, under the eyes of the Brethren who read there, what profit is there in those ridiculous monsters, in that marvellous and deformed comeliness, that comely deformity? To what purposes are those unclean apes, those fierce lions, those monstrous centaurs, those half men, those striped tigers, those fighting knights, those hunters winding their horns? Many bodies are there seen under one head, or again, many heads to a single body. Here is a four-footed beast with a serpent's tail; there a fish with a beast's head. Here again the forepart of a horse trails half a goat behind it, or a horned beast bears the hinder quarters of a horse. In short, so many and so marvelous are the varieties of divers shapes on every hand, that we are more tempted to read in the marble than in our books, and to

[6] For an excellent discussion of the areligious aspect of Romanesque art, see Meyer Schapiro, "On the Aesthetic Attitude in Romanesque Art," *Art and Thought: Essays in Honor of Ananda K. Coomaraswamy* (New York, 1947), pp. 130–150.

spend the whole day in wondering at these things rather than meditating the law of God.[7]

Although the obvious attraction of such sculptures, to which even St. Bernard admitted, resulted in the banning of figurative carving in the churches of his newly founded Cistercian order, the penchant for fantasies, drolleries, and grotesques persisted throughout Gothic manuscripts (No. 66) in capitals, choir stalls, roof bosses, corbels, and misericordes.

The last major period of medieval art, perjoratively labeled "Gothic" by Renaissance humanists, who considered its art forms barbaric, is even more diverse than the Romanesque. It may be considered as beginning about 1140 with the construction of the choir of the Abbey of Saint-Denis. But for arts other than architecture and monumental sculpture, a gothic style, properly speaking, does not make its appearance until about 1200. In the same way, the termination of the Late Gothic and the beginning of the Renaissance are equally vague. The international Gothic style coexists with early Renaissance developments in Italy during the first third of the fifteenth century (No. 109); Late Gothic gives way to the Renaissance in France about 1450 with the work of Fouquet (No. 111); and Albrecht Dürer makes the dramatic transition from Late Medieval to Renaissance in his painted and graphic works at the beginning of the sixteenth century in Germany.

The Gothic period was one of stark contrasts and of momentous political, economic and social changes. The crusades continued and monarchies and principalities constantly warred with each other, while at the same time the allied cults of the Virgin and of chivalry reached their highest expressions in practice and in art (Nos. 59, 71–73, 78–83). The period witnessed the reemergence of the cities, the growth of the bourgeois and mercantile class, the transferral of learning from monastic centers to urban universities, and the building of the great Gothic cathedrals.

The cathedral typifies the complex transformations of church and society which took place between 1150 and 1250. The Romanesque church was essentially monastic, a defensive haven on a pilgrimage road. By the vigor of its forms it was a symbol of the Church Militant during the period of the early Crusades. The most powerful and influential monasteries in Europe during the twelfth century, the abbeys of Cluny and Cîteaux, were situated in peaceful Burgundian valleys. But the Gothic cathedrals of Chartres, Laon, Reims, and Amiens were urban; they dominated the town and the surrounding countryside. As originally conceived with multiple spires reaching into the sky, the cathedral was a jewel set in the medieval city, a vision of the Heavenly City of Jerusalem. The buildings themselves were no longer composed of the massive, additive volumes characteristic of Romanesque churches, but were more unified, organic units enveloped in a lacework of flying buttresses and pinnacles. The result was a building which expanded

[7] Quoted in Holt, 1957, p. 21.

into the space around it, both vertically and horizontally, and into which space penetrated and circulated around the filigree of an intricate skeleton.

The mystical vision of the faith in the thirteenth century, exemplified by the scholastic resolution of theological issues and by an aura of serene self-assurance, called for buildings expressive of the new attitudes. This expression took the form of the ordered, logical resolution of supporting systems, the unencumbered interior with its uplifting vertical space, and the quality of ethereal purple light emanating from the stained-glass windows. These manifestations were in turn made possible by technological innovations, which resolved the problems posed by Romanesque churches. The combined use of rib vaults and pointed arches removed the need for load-bearing walls, allowing the spaces between supporting piers to be voided and filled with thin membranes of translucent glass.[8]

The attitudes and forms that can be seen in the architecture of the Gothic period permeate the other arts. Thus boxwood combs, among the smallest and most personal of objects (Nos. 85–86), reflect the late, flamboyant Gothic preoccupation with elaborate tracery and the spatial penetration of forms in their lace-like filigree. Similarly, Gothic statuary tends to emerge from the restrictions of the block of material by asserting its independent, swaying axis (No. 91). Monumental sculpture tends to detach itself from its architectural context and becomes one of many punctuating elements in a screen before the structural fabric (as in the portals at Reims or Amiens). Even reliefs become more spatially articulated. Figures emerge almost to the point of complete detachment and do not present themselves frontally or in profile, but turn on their axis to present a three-quarter view (No. 62). Draperies are used to impart greater substantiality to the figure (Nos. 91, 95) and become independent, expressive elements in their own right (Nos. 91, 93, 96).

The vast architectural and artistic output in the century and a half between 1200 and 1350 resulted in a certain uniformity of style, a lack of differentiation of personalities, and a repetitiveness of scenes. The encrustation of cathedral portals with extensive complexes of sculpture, the countless historiated medallions in the windows of Sainte Chapelle, the production of numerous moralized Bibles with over a thousand illustrations each, and the profusion of carved ivory panels (Nos. 74–77) all testify to the presence of ateliers in which art was virtually mass-produced during the Gothic period.

As a result of the social changes that took place from the beginning of the twelfth century through the fifteenth, the entire patronage structure was

---

[8] Few books capture the contrasting moods of Romanesque and Gothic architecture and their contemporary historical and literary currents as well as Henry Adams' *Mont-Saint-Michel and Chartres* (New York, 1933). Other important assessments of the role and meaning of the Gothic cathedral may be found in Otto von Simson, *The Gothic Cathedral* (New York, 1956); Hans Jantzen, *High Gothic* (New York, 1962); Paul Frankl, *Gothic Architecture* (Harmondsworth and Baltimore, 1962); and Erwin Panofsky, *Gothic Architecture and Scholasticism* (New York, 1957).

transformed. Demands for different kinds of objects arose. Increasing emphasis was placed on private devotion and on the direct intercession of the
Virgin in behalf of the individual. Thus, in the fourteenth century, numerous
ivory diptychs, tabernacles, and statuettes were produced for private household altars (Nos. 71–77), and countless small Prayerbooks and Books of
Hours were written and illuminated for use in personal devotions (Nos. 87,
103–108, 111, 112).

At the same time, the themes of secular literature from the early medieval
epics, the *chansons de geste,* the Arthurian romances (No. 79), the *Roman
de la Rose* (Nos. 81–83), the *Minnesänge* (No. 81), and other legends of
chivalry and courtly love assumed a greater importance in artistic productions, partly as a result of increasingly secular patronage. We therefore find
a profusion of ivory writing tablets, mirror backs (Nos. 81–83), combs (No.
84), and marriage caskets for jewels (Nos. 78–80) decorated with scenes
either depicting specific incidents from the literary cycles or more generally
related to the theme of courtly love.[9] Scenes such as the Labors of the
Months, though often used to illustrate the calendars of manuscripts or to
give a temporal context to the sculptural ensembles of Romanesque and
Gothic portals, also provided an opportunity to exploit genre scenes for their
realistic detail and natural settings, as in the calendar illustrations of the
Très Riches Heures and in sets of tapestries (No. 114). Secular motifs creep
into the marginal illustrations of Books of Hours (No. 66), where all manner
of animals and grotesque beasts enact scenes from proverbs and fables and
depict comic, derisive, and even obscene situations.[10] In the later Gothic
period, these marginalia become full-fledged scenes, usually complementing
the principal miniatures (No. 107). Eventually they develop into extraordinary illusionistic representations of birds, insects, flowers, and still-life
objects (No. 108). The development of greater realism in the treatment of
space and landscape in manuscript miniatures after 1400 parallels a new
and more secular attitude towards the illuminated manuscript, including the
Book of Hours. These volumes are no longer the embellished Word of God,
but are now regarded as *objets d'art* and are referred to as *joyaux,* or jewels,
in the itemized inventories of such patrons and collectors as John, Duke of
Berry.

THE ART OF THE CHURCH TREASURIES

Abbeys and churches decorated with a multitude of sculpted reliefs and
capitals are among the most monumental and complex manifestations of the

[9] For discussions of literary themes in medieval art, see Roger S. Loomis, "The Allegorical Siege in the Art of the Middle Ages," *American Journal of Archeology,* ser. 2,
XXIII, no. 3 (1919), 255–269, and *Arthurian Legends in Medieval Art* (New York, 1938);
and David J. A. Ross, "Allegory and Romance on a Medieval French Marriage Casket,"
Journal of the Warburg and Courtauld Institute, II (1948), 112–142.

[10] See Lilian M. C. Randall, *Images in the Margins of Gothic Manuscripts* (Berkeley,
1966), for a wide variety of these marginalia.

Christian faith during the Middle Ages. But no less important or spectacular are the innumerable objects on a smaller scale that served in the Christian ritual. A variety of crafts provided clerical and secular patrons alike with illuminated manuscripts, carvings in ivory and boxwood, metalwork, and goldwork, to furnish their churches, private chapels, and homes. By virtue of their precious materials, their superb craftsmanship, and their stylistic and iconographical innovations, many of these artifacts occupy places of considerable importance in the history of medieval art.

The variety of liturgical objects is endless. Religious manuscripts such as Gospels, Bibles, Sacramentaries, or Breviaries were often encased in beautifully wrought metalwork covers set with precious stones, ivories, or enamels (No. 37). These books were often displayed on the high altar together with elaborate altar crosses (No. 43) with the body of the crucified Christ (Nos. 44–46) and flanked by candlesticks (No. 47). For the processional at the beginning of the Mass there were processional crosses (No. 42), maces, and bishops' croziers (Nos. 40–42). The preparation for the Mass required liturgical combs (No. 31) and ewers or aquamaniles (No. 69) from which to pour water for cleansing the hands. Ciboria, chalices, pyxes (No. 33), and Eucharistic doves (No. 32) were made to contain the Sacrament, the wine, and the Host. Enamel caskets were created to enshrine the relics of saints (Nos. 34–36), and these were exhibited with cult images of the Virgin and Child (No. 56) on the various secondary altars of the churches. Ivory statuettes of the Virgin and Child (No. 72), ivory diptychs, triptychs, and tabernacles or folding shrines (Nos. 71, 74–77) were produced for the private devotions of the nobility in their own chapels.

We cannot help but marvel at the quantity of these objects and at the quality of their workmanship. Many are resplendent with gold and silver, jewels and semiprecious stones. Vestments are made of costly silks, and manuscripts are richly illuminated. But we may also wonder why these things were commissioned by or for the Church, an institution that even in contemporary eyes should have been spending its money in more useful and charitable ways. We may recall St. Bernard's stern admonition:

But I say, as a monk, ask of my brother monks . . . , 'Tell me, ye poor men . . . (if indeed ye be poor), what doeth this gold in *your* sanctuary?' And indeed the bishops have an excuse which monks have not; for we know that they, being debtors to both the wise and the unwise, and unable to excite the devotion of carnal folk by spiritual things, do so by bodily ornaments. But we [monks] who have now come forth from the people; we who have left all the precious and beautiful things of the world for Christ's sake . . . , do we intend to excite by these things? . . . [Men's] eyes are feasted with relics cased in gold, and their purse strings are loosed. They are shown a most comely image of some saint, whom they think all the more saintly that he is the more gaudily painted. Men run to kiss him, and are invited to give; there is more admiration for his comeliness than veneration for his sanctity. Hence the church is adorned with gemmed crowns of light—nay, with lustres like cart wheels, girt all around with lamps, but no less brilliant with the precious stones that stud them. Moreover, we see candelabras standing like trees of massive bronze, fashioned with marvelous subtlety of art, and glistening no less brightly with gems than the lights they carry. . . . The church is resplendent in her walls, beggarly in her poor; she clothes her stones in gold, and leaves her sons naked; the rich man's eye is fed at the expense of the indigent. . . . For God's sake, if men are not ashamed of these follies, why at least do they not shrink from the expense?[11]

The most effective rebuttal was given by Bernard's illustrious contemporary, Abbot Suger of Saint-Denis, whose lavish patronage was responsible for the rebuilding of the royal Abbey of Saint-Denis, resulting in the first example of the Gothic style. Suger's desire to embellish the new abbey went beyond the mere architectural fabric to the provision of new liturgical objects, new reliquaries, chalices, and altar frontals. The Abbot recorded all his accomplishments in his book, "On What Was Done under His Administration." In this he reflected typically thirteenth-century views, but his reasons given for the rich adornment of the new furnishings of the Abbey reflect a long-standing attitude concerning the decoration of religious objects. According to Suger, the new cast and gilded doors "being nobly bright . . . should brighten the minds so that they may travel through the true lights to the True Light where Christ is the true door." Such embellishment to illumine the mind and to encourage lofty thoughts was also carried out on the high altar, of which Suger wrote:

Often we contemplate out of sheer affection for the church, our mother, these different ornaments, both new and old. . . . Thus when—out of my delight in the beauty of the house of God—the loveliness of the many colored gems has called me away from external cares, and worthy meditation has induced me to reflect, transferring that which is material to that which is immaterial, on the diversity of the sacred virtues; then it seems to me that I see myself dwelling, as it were, in some strange region of the universe which neither exists entirely in the slime of the earth nor in the purity of Heaven; and that by the grace of God, I can be transposed from this inferior to that higher world in an anagogical manner.[12]

Not only for Abbot Suger in the twelfth century, but also for countless abbots, bishops, and emperors before and after him, the decoration of liturgical objects served to elevate the mind and invoke more sublime thoughts and meditations. Books of gospels, richly illuminated as befitting the Word of God (No. 23) and encased in jeweled bindings, were the resplendent symbols of the presence of Christ. They were carried in processions and en-

[11] Quoted in Holt, 1957, pp. 19–21. For the complete text, see G. G. Coulton, *Life in the Middle Ages* (Cambridge, 1930), IV, 72–76.

[12] Quoted in Holt, 1957, p. 30. See also the introduction to Erwin Panofsky, *Abbot Suger on the Abbey Church of Saint-Denis and Its Art Treasures* (Princeton, 1946); reprinted in Panofsky, *Meaning in the Visual Arts* (Garden City, N.Y., 1955), pp. 108–145.

throned on the altar.[13] The same could be said of the other objects used for the ritual of the Church, where no luxury was too great to adorn these visual manifestations of a higher purpose. Thus a gleaming, finely worked processional cross (No. 42), a multicolored enamel Eucharistic dove (No. 32) and the sparkling lights and glowing colors of a bishop's crozier (Nos. 40–41) were appropriately "nobly bright," serving to "brighten the minds" of the beholder.

THE MEDIEVAL ARTIST

In any discussion or presentation of works of art from the Middle Ages one is confronted by the prevailing anonymity of the medieval artist. The present exhibition is no exception: only one work is signed (Tirolus Iafarinus, No. 42) and only a handful are close to the style or workshop of known artisans (G. Alpais, No. 36; Claus Sluter, No. 91; Jacquemart de Hesdin, No. 103; Tilman Riemenschneider, No. 100; Bernt Notke, No. 102; Jean Fouquet and Jean Colombe, No. 111; and Jean Bourdichon, No. 112). More frequent mention is made of artists who are anonymous, but who have been given convenient names after their principal works, such as the Luçon Master (Nos. 103–105), the Boucicaut Master (No. 106), and the Bedford Master (Nos. 103, 107).

This anonymity stems from the nature of medieval patronage and from the attitudes held by the artisans themselves. In the Middle Ages, members of the church, court, or nobility commissioned works and specified most of the details, which the artisans then dutifully carried out. It was previously believed that artisans before the Gothic period were monks, but there is now some evidence to suggest that a number of them were lay artisans who traveled about from one monastery to another.[14] But whatever their station, monk or lay artisan, and whatever their trade, scribe, illuminator, sculptor, metalsmith, or architect, they were primarily concerned with carrying out their commissions, building, maintaining, and embellishing the house of God and its artifacts without seeking recognition for their labors. Thus documentary references to medieval works of art may specify for whom the work was made, but rarely mention who the artist was. Abbot Suger, who watched over every detail of the rebuilding and refurbishing of Saint-Denis, mentions that the enameled pedestal decorated with the four Evangelists which supported the cross for the High Altar was completed by "several goldsmiths from Lorraine—at times five, at other times seven," but gives no

[13] Peter Metz, *The Golden Gospels of Echternach: Codex Aureus Epternancensis* (New York, 1957), pp. 19–22, and Hanns Swarzenski, *Monuments of Romanesque Art: The Art of Church Treasures in North Western Europe* (London and Chicago, 1954), contain important discussions of the significance of the art of the Church treasures.

[14] G. G. Coulton, *Medieval Faith and Symbolism* (New York, 1928), chs. 1–4, proposes that the lay artisan was always in preponderance, a view supported by Virginia W. Egbert, *The Mediaeval Artist at Work* (Princeton, 1967).

indication of their identity.[15] When names of artists do occur in documents, especially in the later Middle Ages, there is often no way of identifying their works. Only when artisans signed and dated their productions do we have a sure indication of identity and time, but the attribution of other, similar works to these artists or to their milieus must depend on careful stylistic analysis.

In the few cases where artisans did sign and date their works we are provided with valuable insights into their status and attitudes. Normally such inscriptions are in the form of simple signatures and a date, as in the copy of the Apocalypse now in the Cathedral at Borgo da Osma in Spain, signed by the scribe "Petrus clericus" and a painter "Martinus" and dated 1086.[16] Often the inscriptions are in the form of humble pleas, such as the one made by Tirolus Iafarinus on his cross (No. 42) that the beholder might remember him in his prayers. Sometimes artists showed themselves at work. The lay artisan Engelramus represented himself and his son Redolfus on an ivory panel of a casket now in Leningrad, the illuminator Hildebert depicted himself in lay raiment with his apprentice Everwin in two manuscripts of about 1140, and in an early twelfth-century book Fra Rufilus, a monk, painted himself illuminating an initial inhabited by dragons and grotesques.[17]

Some of the early inscriptions manifest an awareness of achievement. In a Bible made at Léon in 960, the scribe Sanctio and his master Florentius, both dressed in clerical habits, show themselves toasting each other and thanking God for the successful completion of the volume.[18] We can detect an element of pride in the monumental "GISLEBERTUS HOC FECIT" carved beneath the feet of the *Majestas Domini* in the Autun tympanum of about 1130 and in the even stronger inscription by Gilabertus of Toulouse on some jamb figures from the portal of Saint Etienne, which translates something like "Gilabertus, not just any man, created me."[19] But the height of self-esteem, and indeed a prefiguration of the new relationship of the artisan to society in the Gothic period, is achieved in the third quarter of the twelfth century by the English monk Eadwine, who not only prefaces the psalter he inscribed with a full page self-portrait, which was unique enough, but also enframed it with the following inimitable conceit: "Scribe, nay Prince of Scribes am I. Neither my praises nor my fame shall ever die. Let the letters traced by my pen declare the man I am."[20]

[15] Quoted in Holt, 1957, p. 28.

[16] André Grabar and Carl Nordenfalk, *Early Medieval Painting* (Lausanne, 1957), p. 168.

[17] Egbert, 1967, Plate III, fig. 5 and pl. V, and pl. IV.

[18] Grabar and Nordenfalk, 1957, p. 165, illus. p. 167.

[19] Denis Grivot and George Zarnecki, *Gislebertus: Sculpteur d'Autun* (Paris, 1960), p. 13, n. 1. For the St. Etienne statues, see Arthur K. Porter, *Romanesque Sculpture of the Pilgrimage Roads* (Boston, 1923), Vol. IV, pls. 434–435.

[20] This frontispiece is in the so-called Eadwine Psalter, Cambridge, Trinity College Library, MS. R.17.I; see C. R. Dodwell, *The Canterbury School of Illumination, 1066–1200* (Cambridge, 1954), p. 36.

The profound transformations which took place in Europe with the advent of the Gothic era, beginning slowly in the twelfth century and reaching full maturity in the thirteenth, had a considerable effect not only on artistic production, but also on the relationship of the artist to society. The result was significant growth in the number of lay artisans as opposed to monastic ones. Thus we find with increasing frequency representations of clerics and lay artisans working side by side, as in the case of the author dictating to a lay scribe or illuminator in the frontispiece of the Toledo Bible now in the Morgan Library (MS. M.240) and a clerical scribe and a lay mural-painter working in a miniature from a thirteenth-century pattern book in Vienna (Nationalbibliothek, MS. 507).[21] No doubt talented monks continued to produce works of art,[22] but by the fourteenth century, lay artisans were forming their own ateliers, becoming members of local craft guilds, and instituting rigorous systems of apprenticeship for the instruction of new members. Scribes and illuminators, among them Jean Pucelle, congregated in the sector of Paris around the Porte Saint-Denis, then known as the "Porte aux Peintres," and in the rue des Ecrivins.[23] Names of individual artists were recorded with increasing frequency in inventories and accounts, and as early as 1304 the title of "Peintre du roi de France" was created.[24] Toward the end of the fourteenth century, an artist appointed to the royal household, Gerard d'Orleans, accompanied his monarch, Jean de France, into prison in England after the battle of Poitiers, and the illuminator Jacquemart de Hesdin (No. 103), who had killed a fellow artisan in a brawl, was pardoned through the intercession of his patron, John, Duke of Berry.[25] The Limbourg brothers, the illuminators of the *Très Riches Heures*, were so sure of their position in the Duke's household that they were able to present him with a practical joke, a block of wood painted to simulate a richly bound manuscript.[26]

Along with an increased awareness of the value of quality and uniqueness, there developed a desire to show how things are done for the benefit of those who wish to learn a particular craft. One of the most important manifestations of this desire to instruct was an early twelfth-century treatise entitled *De diversis artibus*. It was written by the Benedictine monk Theophilus, who, it is believed, was actually the German metalsmith Roger of

[21] For M.240 see *Treasures from the Pierpont Morgan Library, Fiftieth Annual Exhibition* (New York, 1957), No. 21, pl. 20; for the Vienna manuscript see Egbert, 1967, pl. IX.

[22] See Egbert, 1967, pl. X–XXXI. Of these representations of artisans at work, dating from the thirteenth to the fifteenth century, only four show monks.

[23] Kathleen Morand, *Jean Pucelle* (Oxford, 1962), p. 2, and H. Fierens-Gevaert, *Les Très Belles Heures de Jean de France, duc de Berry* (Brussels, 1924), p. 7.

[24] Paul Durrieu in André Michel, ed., *L'histoire de l'art depuis les premiers temps chrétiens jusqu'à nos jours*, Vol. III–1 (Paris, 1907), 103.

[25] For Gérard d'Orleans see *ibid.*, p. 105; for Jacquemart de Hesdin see Fierens-Gevaert, 1924, pp. 38–39.

[26] Paul Durrieu, *Les Très Riches Heures de Jean de France, duc de Berry* (Paris, 1904), p. 17.

Helmarshausen (Nos. 43, 45), active around Paderborn between 1110 and 1140.[27] This treatise, like a number of earlier Byzantine manuals and later fifteenth-century manuscripts on the arts, was a compilation of recipes and technical instructions for painting, glassworking, and metalworking. Today, it provides valuable insights into the processes employed by medieval artisans in the fabrication of artifacts. Other insights into the actual artistic process may be found in contemporary representations of artisans at work, most often depicted in manuscript illustrations, in which we find painters, illuminators, architects, metalworkers, stone-carvers, and polychromers at their tasks.[28] We also learn much of the artist's selective process and of his *modus operandi* from sketchbooks and model books that have survived.[29] Among the most remarkable and revealing of these is the notebook of the thirteenth-century French architect Villard de Honnecourt, who not only sought to instruct, but also to record, those things which he deemed noteworthy.[30] It is in such personalities as Abbot Suger, Gislebertus, Eadwine, and Villard de Honnecourt that we find an emerging identity, an assertion of individuality, and an awareness of the importance of the artist in an historical and social sense. In them we find the precursors of the Renaissance, the beginning of the transformation of the medieval "artisan" into the Renaissance "artist."

In contrast to the twentieth century, with its bewildering political, social, economic, and international problems, the Middle Ages was subject to a dominant force in the working out of human destiny: the spiritual and temporal power of the Christian Church. This does not mean that medieval man was better than modern man, or that he was more nobly motivated, for people presumably have remained much the same. During the Middle Ages, people lived within a different framework; throughout Christendom, in spite of multifarious differences and ideological squabbles, they had a universal belief in a common spiritual center.

Thus medieval art mirrors Christian faith at all levels in its emphasis on religious narrative and symbolism. Much of it was didactic, reminding the worshiper of the incidents of the Bible and the precepts of the Faith, while some of it served as political propaganda in the service of the Church and Empire. But beneath the religious and imperial iconography, beneath the more subtle meanings of particular choices of symbols or forms, there lurks

---

[27] For a review of the problems concerning this identification and for the treatise itself, see John G. Hawthorne and Cyril S. Smith, *On Divers Arts: The Treatise of Theophilus* (Chicago, 1963).

[28] Egbert, 1967, contains an extensive compilation of these representations.

[29] For a selection of sketchbooks, see R. W. Scheller, *A Survey of Medieval Model Books* (Haarlem, 1963).

[30] See *ibid.*, pp. 88–93, for a brief discussion of the Villard de Honnecourt notebook and recent bibliography.

the artist himself, the anonymous servant of God who occasionally made his presence felt, stated his name, and made his claim on posterity.

In the legacy of the medieval artist, in the unfolding picture of medieval art, we read the story of man's absorption in his faith, of his growing independence from dogma, and of his increasing assertion of his own individuality.

Plates

16 ENAMEL PLAQUE
BAPTISM OF CHRIST
Byzantine, 12th c.

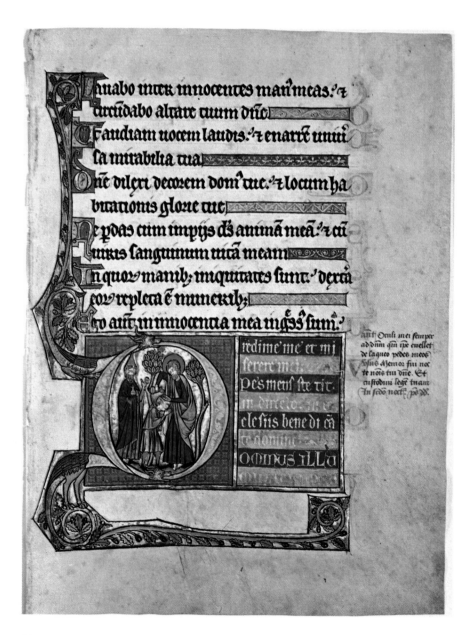

64 FOLIO FROM A PSALTER
INITIAL WITH ANOINTING OF DAVID?
French, c. 1280

103 BOOK OF HOURS
ADORATION OF THE MAGI
French, 1405–1410

109 GRADUAL

MARTYRDOM OF ST. LAWRENCE
Northern Italian, Lombardy, 2nd quarter of 15th c.

3 STEELYARD WEIGHT
ENTHRONED EMPEROR, CONSTANTINE?
Late Roman, 5th–6th c.

1 FRAGMENT OF A PYXIS
DIONYSUS AND PANTHER
Late Roman, 3rd–4th c.

2 CARPENTERS AT WORK
Late Roman, 3rd–4th c.

4 FRAGMENT OF A SARCOPHAGUS
THE GOOD SHEPHERD
Late Roman, late 3rd–early 4th c.

6 ECCLESIA REWARDING BASILIDES?
  Coptic, 4th–5th c.

11 CRUCIFIXION
Byzantine, 10th c.

13 DEPOSITION
Italo-Byzantine, 12th c.

17 ENAMEL MEDALLION
ST. MARK
Byzantine, 12th c.

19 FOLIO FROM GOSPELS
ST. MATTHEW
Byzantine, 12th c.

21 BOW FIBULA
Merovingian, 5th–6th c.

22 BUCKLE
Merovingian, 7th c.

23 FOLIO FROM GOSPELS
FRONTISPIECE OF GOSPELS OF ST. JOHN
German, *c*.950–975

23 FOLIO FROM GOSPELS
FIRST PAGE OF GOSPELS OF ST. JOHN
German, c.950–975

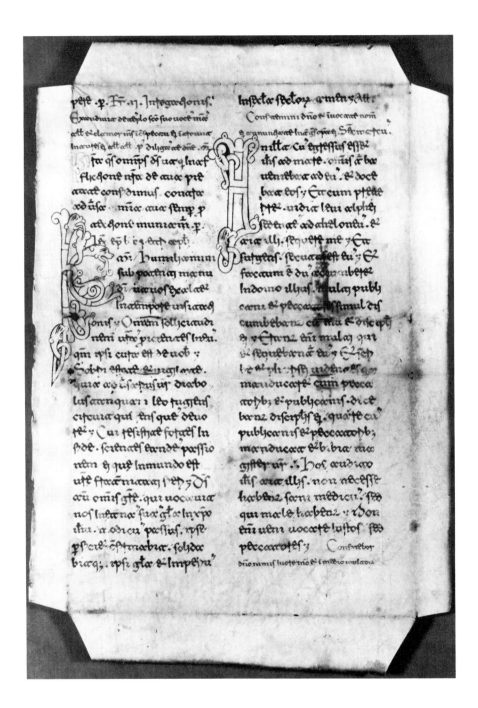

25 FOLIO FROM A SACRAMENTARY
Southern Italian, Benevento, c.1100

INCIPIT SCDA PARS EXPLA
NATIONIS BĪ GREGORII PP
P CONTEMPLATIONĒ ASSVP
TE. SVP LIBRV BĪ IOB IO
Ē A DONO X VSQ: A OFINĒ

VID
MIRV̄
SI ETR
NA

saṗientia dei conspici non ualeat. quando ipsa
quoqʒ; inuisibilia que p eam sunt condita huma
nis oculis comprehendi non possunt. In rebus
ergo creatis discimus creatorem omnium quan
ta humilitate ueneremur. ut in hac uita usur
pare sibi de omnipotentis dei spetie mens huma
na nichil audeat. quod solum electis suis premi
um in subsequenti remuneratione seruat. Vn
de bene postquam dictum est. absondita est ab
oculis omnium uiuentium. ideo subinfertur.
Uolucres celi quoqʒ; latet. In scriptura enim sa
cta uolucres aliquando in malo. aliquando ue
ro in bono dantur intelligi. Per uolucres quip
pe nonnonquam potestates aerie designantur.
bonorum studiis aduerse. Vnde ueritatis ore di
citur. quoniam semen quod secus uiam cecidit.
uenerunt uolucres & comederunt illud. Quia
nimirum maligni sp̄s humanas mentes obside
res. dum cogitationes noxias ingerunt. uerbū

LIBER   NVMERI

mifit adbalaam ut uentret & maledicerer   **INCIPIT LIAGEDABER**
ifrl' & obuiauit. illi angeluf eua ginato gladio.
Fornicati funt ex populo cu machanitis. & oc   **IDEST NVMERVS**
cidit fines zambri cum madianite & mor
tui funt. Dic dns ad moyfen ut pcutiant   **OCVTVS EST + DNS**
machanitas. Precepit dns moyfi . a . xx. an
no & fupra confiderare poptm & numerati   **AD MOYSEN IN DESER**
funt de Dcc xxx. I thi lcui ex quib; amra
& uxor ci' iocabeth que pepit aaron & moy   **TO SINAI IN TABERNA**
fen & maria qui confiderau funt ab uno
menfe & fupra . xx. m. mt'. Accepit moyfes   **CVLO FOE**
thm filiu naue & impofint fup cum manuf
coram omni poptm fic conftituit illi dns ho   **DERIS**
Dicit dns moyfi ut parpiat poptm de facrifi
cus & hoftiis. Que m die pafche offerri   Prima die menfis fecundi. anno altero egrcf
debcat oftendit. Que m pentecoften.   fionis coz ex egypto dicens. Tollite fumma

28 BIBLE
BEGINNING OF THE BOOK OF NUMBERS
English, 12th c.

30 MARGINAL ILLUSTRATION FROM A BIBLE
CHRIST IN MAJESTY
Northern Italian or Sicilian, *c.*1260

30 MARGINAL ILLUSTRATION FROM A BIBLE
ELKANAH AND HIS WIVES
Northern Italian or Sicilian, *c.*1260

29 FOLIO FROM A PSALTER
BETRAYAL OF CHRIST
Southern German, 13th c.

24 LION
   German, c.1050

69 AQUAMANILE
   German or Flemish, 14th c.

32 EUCHARISTIC DOVE
French, Limoges, 13th c.

34 RELIQUARY CASKET
French, Limoges, 13th c.

37 PLAQUE FROM BOOKCOVER
CHRIST IN MAJESTY
French, Limoges, *c.*1250

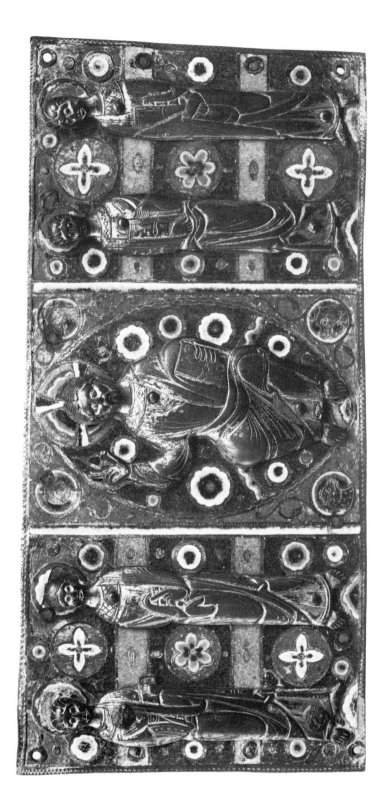

35 PLAQUE FROM RELIQUARY CASKET
CHRIST IN MAJESTY AND FOUR EVANGELISTS
French, Limoges, 2nd quarter of 13th c.

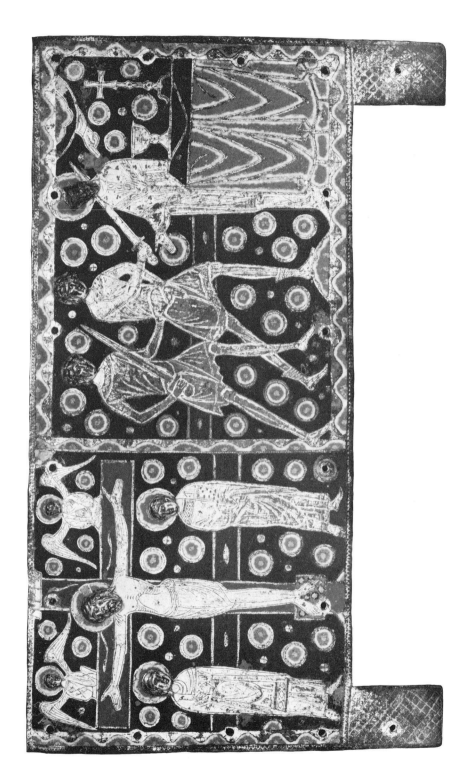

36 PLAQUE FROM RELIQUARY CASKET
CRUCIFIXION, MARTYRDOM OF THOMAS À BECKET
French, Limoges, *c*.1220–1225

38 ST. JOSEPH
French, Limoges, 13th c.

41 CROZIER HEAD
ANNUNCIATION
French, Limoges, 13th c.

42 PROCESSIONAL CROSS
Northeastern Italian, first half of 12th c.

43 STANDING CROSS
Mosan or German, 12th–13th c.

45 CORPUS CHRISTI
Mosan or German, 12th c.

45 SIDE VIEW OF OPPOSITE

44 CORPUS CHRISTI
French, Limoges, 13th c.

46 CORPUS CHRISTI
Spanish, 13th c.

47 CANDLESTICK
German or Mosan, late 12th c.

48 SIGNS OF THE EVANGELISTS AND ROSETTE
Northeastern Italian, 12th c.

49 DOUBLE CAPITAL
GRIFFINS
Spanish, early 13th c.

50 CAPITAL
VIRGIN AND CHILD; JOURNEY OF THE MAGI
French, 12th c.

54 ST. PETER
South Central French, first half of 12th c.

53 COLUMN WITH ADOSSED SAINTS: ST. SIMON
Spanish, Santiago de Compostela, 12th c.

51 CORBEL
MUSICIAN PLAYING VIOL
Southern French, Provence, 12th c.

52 ELDER OF THE APOCALYPSE
Spanish, early 13th c.

55 HEAD OF A MAN
Southern French, St. Gilles-
du-Gard, c.1160

57 HEAD OF A KING
French, Ile-de-France? mid or 3rd quarter of 12th c.

60 YOUTHFUL HEAD
French, Reims? 2nd quarter of 13th c.

61 CANDLEHOLDER OR ALTAR SUPPORT
KNEELING PAGE
Southern Italian, mid 13th c.

56 ENTHRONED MADONNA AND CHILD
Spanish, Catalonia, 13th c.

59 ENTHRONED MADONNA AND CHILD
French, Lorraine, 1330–1350

58 ANGEL
French, Burgundy, end of 13th c.

62 FRAGMENT OF SARCOPHAGUS
DANIEL STANDING BETWEEN TWO LIONS
Northeastern Italian, *c.*1340–60

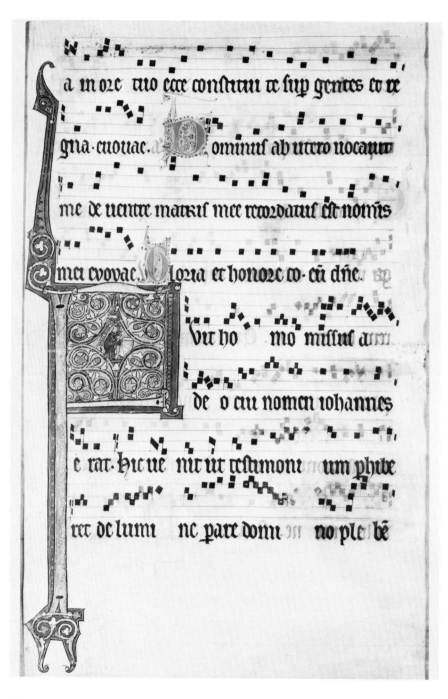

63 FOLIO FROM AN ANTIPHONAL
INITIAL WITH ANNUNCIATION TO ZACHARIAS
Flemish, Cambron, 13th c.

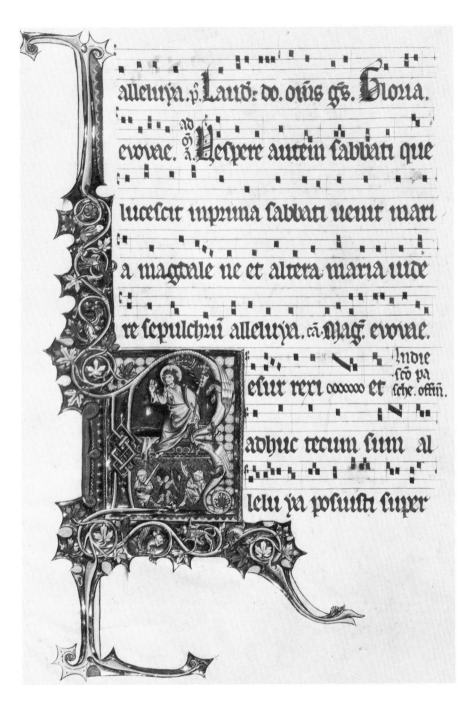

alleuya. ꝯ. Laudo do. oꝰus gꝭ. Gloua. ad euoue. ꝯ. a. Uespere autem sabbati que lucesat imprima sabbati uenit maria magdale ne et altera maria uide re sepulchꝛu alleuya. ca. Mag. euoue. Indie sco pa sche. offin. esur reri oooooo et adhuc tecum sum al leluya posuisti super

65 FOLIO FROM A GRADUAL
INITIAL WITH RESURRECTION
German, early 14th c.

70 CROZIER HEAD
VIRGIN AND CHILD; CRUCIFIXION
French, 14th c.

72 STATUETTE OF VIRGIN AND CHILD
French, 14th c.

71 TABERNACLE WITH VIRGIN AND CHILD
ATELIER OF TABERNACLES OF THE VIRGIN
French, 14th c.

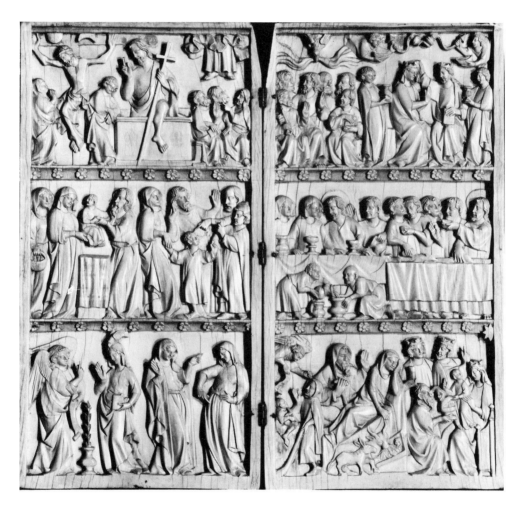

74 IVORY DIPTYCH

SCENES OF LIFE OF CHRIST AND LIFE OF THE VIRGIN

French, first half of 14th c.

77 IVORY DIPTYCH
NATIVITY AND CRUCIFIXION
French, mid 14th c.

75 IVORY DIPTYCH
SCENES FROM LIFE OF CHRIST
French, mid or second half of 14th c.

76 IVORY DIPTYCH
VIRGIN AND CHLD; CRUCIFIXION
French, 14th c.

78 COFFRET
French, end of 14th c.

79 TOP OF CASKET BELOW

79 MARRIAGE CASKET WITH AMOROUS SCENES
   English, 14th c.

82 MIRROR BACK
AMOROUS COUPLES
French, 14th c.

80 TOP OF A CASKET
JOUSTING SCENE
French, 14th c.

81 MIRROR BACK
SIEGE OF CASTLE OF LOVE
French, c.1320–50

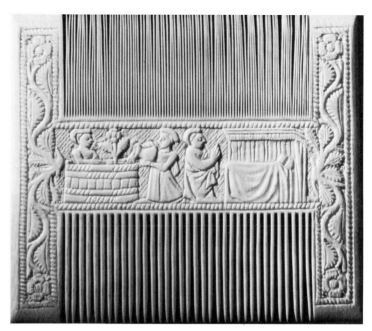

84 IVORY COMB
PREPARATION FOR THE JOUST
French? 15th c.

84 REVERSE OF ABOVE
THE JOUST
French? 15th c.

85 BOXWOOD COMB
French, late 15th c.

86 BOXWOOD COMB
French, late 15th c.

89 THE LORD REPRIMANDING ADAM AND EVE
Franco-Italian or Lombard, late 14th c.

92 PAIR OF STATUETTES
BISHOPS
Dutch, Utrecht, c.1500

90 IVORY STATUETTES
   MOURNING VIRGIN AND ST. JOHN
   French, Burgundy? *c.*1400

91 PROPHET
WORKSHOP OF CLAUS SLUTER
French, Burgundy, early 15th c.

88 CANDLEHOLDER
German, early 15th c.

94 VIRGIN AND CHILD
Flemish, Malines? late 15th c.

93 VIRGIN AND CHILD
Dutch, Utrecht? late 15th or early 16th c.

95 ANNUNCIATE VIRGIN
Flemish, last quarter of 15th c.

101 ST. ROCH AND THE ANGEL
SCHOOL OF RIEMENSCHNEIDER?
German, c.1500

102 ST. MICHAEL?
German, Lubeck, c.1500

104 BOOK OF HOURS
DEATH OF THE VIRGIN
Luçon Master
French, 1405–1410

105 BOOK OF HOURS
ANNUNCIATION
French, 1405–1420

106 BOOK OF HOURS
DAVID PRAYING
Boucicaut Atelier
French, 1410–20

107 BOOK OF HOURS
VIRGIN AND CHILD IN ROSE ARBOR
Northern French or Flemish, *c.*1440

109 GRADUAL

ASCENSION OF THE VIRGIN
Northern Italian, Lombardy, 2nd quarter of 15th c.

INCOMINCIANO ISONETTI
ELECANZONE DIMESERE FR
ANCESCHO PETRARCHA
POETA FIORENTINO FELICI
TER INCIPIT :~ .j.

OI CHASCOLTATE
inrime sparse elsono
Diquei sospiri ondio
nutriua elcore
Insulmio primo gio
umile errore
Quandera inparte al
truo daquel chisono
Deluario stile inchio
piango & ragiono

fra leuane speranze eluan dolore
oue sia chi per prouua intenda amore
Spero trouar pieta non che perdono
Aben ueggio or sicome alpopol tutto
fauola fui gran tempo onde souente
Dime medesmo meco miuergogno
Et delmio uaneggiar uergogna e elfrutto
Elpentersi elconoscier chiaramente
che quanto piace almondo e breue sogno

110 PETRARCH, *Trionfi, Soneta e Canzoni*
INITIAL WITH PETRARCH
Italian, Florence? late 15th c.

111 FOLIO FROM A BOOK OF HOURS
CHRIST BEFORE PILATE
Close to Jean Fouquet
French, Touraine, 3rd quarter of 15th c.

112 FOLIO FROM A BOOK OF HOURS
KING DAVID
Circle of Jean Bourdichon
French, Touraine? *c.*1500

114 TAPESTRY
WOODCUTTERS
Flemish, Tournai, 1st quarter of 16th c.

Catalogue

In the following notes, some bibliographical references are given in an abbreviated form, either by author and date for books and articles or by city and date for exhibitions, guides, and handbooks. Complete listings for these references may be found in the Bibliography. Where applicable, former collections, previous exhibitions, and published references to the specific object are cited at the end of the entry; every effort has been made to make this information as complete as possible. Absence of any or all of these categories indicates that provenance, earlier exhibitions, or literature are unknown. In all cases, dimensions are given in inches, height preceding width and depth. Symbols appearing after the titles indicate the object is illustrated: a dagger (†) signifies a color plate, an asterisk (*) a black and white one.

1   FRAGMENT OF PYXIS: DIONYSUS AND PANTHER*
     Late Roman, 3rd–4th century
     Ivory, height 4³/₈ in.
     Lent by The Art Museum, Princeton University (62.47)

Probably carved at a time when the Christian religion was gaining followers throughout the Roman Empire, and perhaps even after it was officially recognized as the state religion by Constantine in 317, this fragment of an ivory pyxis, or ointment jar, reflects the full exuberance of paganism in the Late Antique period. The nude figure of Dionysus, the god of wine, is shown leaning on a spear held in his left hand, his right arm carelessly thrown up over his head. A panther appears from behind the god, turning its head to snarl back around the lance. The modeling of the youthful figure reflects the suppleness and soft idealization of larger Hellenistic statuary, yet there is a chunkiness about the forms and a staring quality about the eyes which belie its Late Antique origin. The pose is a common one, found in a number of other similar figures (e.g., Baltimore, 1947, no. 167, Egypt, 4th century; no. 170, Egypt, 4th–5th century; no. 176, Egypt, 4th–5th century), but the treatment of the body is closest to that of a relief of Dionysus in the Walters Art Gallery said to be Alexandrian, 4th century (no. 71.1099; *Ibid.*, no. 166, pl. XVI).

Literature: Record of the Art Museum, Princeton University, XXII, no. 1 (1963), 19.

2   IVORY RELIEF: CARPENTERS AT WORK*
     Late Roman, Alexandria?, 3rd–4th century
     Fragment of a carved ivory tusk, $3^5/8$ x $3^1/8$ in.
     Lent by The Art Museum, Princeton University (56.105)

One of the most difficult problems in the study of the Late Antique period concerns the validity of distinguishing the so-called "Alexandrian style" (see Morey, 1942, and for a critique, Schapiro, 1944). Perhaps the fragment of a carved tusk from Princeton representing two carpenters at work, which was found at Ramleh near Alexandria, lends some support to the thesis. Here we have an illusionistic scene in which two men (only one remains in his entirety) are represented planing a piece of wood. The foreshortened bench on which they work suggests a projection forward into space, while a colonnaded and arcaded fragment of architecture in the background implies a startling degree of spatial recession behind the figure. The relief appears to represent a genre scene, but it has also been suggested that it may depict the building of the ark, a favorite theme among the early Christians referring to man's ultimate salvation. Whether the site of its discovery, the effective illusion of space, and the sympathetic portrayal of the genre scene are sufficient to localize the production of the relief in the region of Alexandria (for such a highly portable object could have been transported there), we must recognize the work of a most accomplished craftsman in the subtle changes of plane, the delicate modeling of the remaining figure, and the naturalness of the carpenter's pose as he bends to his task.

Former Collection: A. M. Friend Jr.
Exhibition: Baltimore, 1947, no. 161, illus., pl. XIII.
Literature: Record of the Art Museum, Princeton University, XVI, no. 1 (1957), 14; Beckwith, 1963, p. 10, fig. 13, p. 47.

3   STEELYARD WEIGHT: ENTHRONED EMPEROR
     CONSTANTINE*
     Late Roman, Gaul?, 5th–6th century
     Bronze, height $4^7/8$ in., weight 22 oz. (approx. 628.5 grams)
     Lent by The Art Museum, Princeton University (55.3257)

The figure of an enthroned, crowned personage holding an orb in his right hand and a shield in his left, and clad in a toga leaving the torso seminude, presents one of the most interesting iconographical problems in the twilight area where Late Antique and Early Christian art fuse with that of the barbarian peoples of northern Europe.

This figurative object is a bronze weight designed to be suspended by the loop above the crown from an adjustable steelyard—one of a number of such objects which have survived from the period of the fifth to the seventh century (see Dumbarton Oaks, 1962, nos. 70–84). Weights in the form of an imperial figure may well have lent an air of reliability and authority to whatever transaction required its use. Of the weights in this particular form (*ibid*, no. 70, p. 60: Berlin Staatliche Museen; Moscow, Historical Museum; and Kherson Museum, USSR), the Princeton example has been shown to contain iconographical details which may most accurately reflect a lost Late Antique statue of Constantine the Great (Alföldi, 1959, pp. 171–179; Ross, 1959, pp. 179–183). The enthroned emperor wearing the toga with the seminude torso could be taken for a Roman emperor, but the orb, originally surmounted by a cross, places the figure in a Christian context. Presumably, then, this representation is of Constantine, yet Ross has pointed out that the earliest known use of the *globus cruciger* occurs on coins of the reigns of Theodosius II and Valentinian III (A.D. 408–454). The problem is further complicated by the presence of two incised decorations on the shield held by the emperor's left hand. The monogram of Christ (No. 8) appears above a heraldic device that has been identified by Alföldi as the curving horns of two confronted goats' heads. The first insignia was not frequently used before the reign of Theodosius I (A.D. 379–395). The latter was the insignia of the "Cornuti," a Teutonic contingent of the Late Roman army that fought with Constantine in the Battle of the Milvian Bridge. It was Constantine's victory in this battle over the forces of Maxentius that paved the way for the establishment of the Christian Roman Empire.

The presence of details that postdate the reign of Constantine, together with the form of dress and the important symbol of the Cornuti in a statuette of crude, even provincial workmanship, suggests that the Princeton weight is a later, perhaps fifth to sixth century copy after a monumental statue of the victorious, enthroned Constantine erected after the Battle of the Milvian Bridge. Perhaps the original was the colossal, but now fragmentary, effigy of the enthroned Constantine that stood in the apse of the Basilica of Constantine in Rome, or some similar statue. In any event, the Princeton weight is an important example of the dissemination of Late Antique forms throughout the Empire (it is said to have been found in Gaul) and of the fusion of Roman, Christian, and barbarian motifs in a single object.

Former Collection: L. Gréau, Paris.
Exhibition: Stanford, 1961.
Literature: Gréau, 1885, pp. 64–65, no. 319; Zahn, 1913–1914, p. 10; Reinach, Vol. V, pt.

2, 1924, 583, no. 6; Waage, 1935, p. 81, fig. 2; *Record of the Art Museum, Princeton University*, XV, no. 1 (1956), 27; *College Art Journal*, XV (1956), 365; Schaffran, 1956, pp. 243–249; Alföldi, 1959, pp. 171–179; Ross, 1959, pp. 179–183.

4   FRAGMENT OF SARCOPHAGUS: GOOD SHEPHERD*
Early Christian, late 3rd–4th century
Marble, $14^1/_2$ x $11^3/_4$ in.
Lent by The Art Museum, Princeton University (52.169)

One of the images most frequently employed by the early Christians and one which embodies many of their beliefs is the representation of the Good Shepherd. We find it in frescoes in the Catacombs of Priscilla and Calixtus, in mosaics in the Mausoleum of Galla Placidia in Ravenna, and as a free-standing statue as in the famous example in the Lateran in Rome. The fragment of a marble sarcophagus from Princeton typifies the usual form of this representation: the youthful, unbearded figure of the shepherd stands with a sheep across his shoulders, while two other sheep of the flock cluster about his feet and a nesting bird and foliage appear above them. The entire group is placed within an architectural frame consisting of spirally fluted Corinthian columns and the gable end of a temple portico.

A time-honored pagan theme dating back to the Moscophorus, or calf-bearer, of Archaic Greece (Akropolis Museum, Athens) and reoccurring in bucolic themes of Hellenistic art, it becomes Christianized in the context of Christ's parable of the Good Shepherd, which offered salvation for the errant soul. Moreover, the conception of Christ in the first centuries of the Christian era also borrowed from the pagan tradition: Christ is seen here as a youthful god, a Christianized Apollo or Orpheus. Indeed, the stance of the Princeton shepherd recalls the slightly swaying pose of a Roman or Greek athlete. At the same time, the bird, symbolic of the soul and of immortality, and the foliage, suggesting the tree of life and paradise, may be further strengthened in their references to salvation and eternal bliss by the temple gateway in which the shepherd stands: a possible portal of the Kingdom of Heaven.

We may conjecture that the sarcophagus from which the Princeton fragment came may have consisted of a series of arcaded niches with other figural groups set within them, perhaps something like the Sarcophagus of Junius Bassus in the Grottoes of St. Peter's in Rome or the Sarcophagus of Bishop Liberius at the church of San Francesco in Ravenna (Volbach, 1961, pp. 141, 174). The style of the Princeton relief evinces the growing provincialization of the Late Antique style in the squatness of the figure, the harsh and erratic quality of drapery folds, and the mere vestige of the drilled technique in the curling locks of hair, derived from earlier Roman art.

Literature: Record of the Art Museum, Princeton University, XII, no. 1 (1953), 38; Jones, 1954, p. 253.

5   FUNERARY STELE: ACOLYTE HOLDING DOVE AND
    BUNCH OF GRAPES
    Egypt, c.300
    Polychromed sandstone, 25³/₄ x 10³/₄ in.
    Lent by the Denver Art Museum (AN–35), Permanent Collection

Recently a number of puzzling stone sculptures, said to have been found in a cemetery, or martyria, at Sheik Ibada, the ancient site of Antinoöpolis in Egypt, have appeared on the art market, and the relief from Denver is one of these. Unfortunately, the absence of archeological information concerning their original situation and the circumstances of their discovery has left a great many questions unanswered.

A starkly frontal and abstracted blocklike figure of a boy is shown standing closely confined by the frame of his rectangular niche in this relief, which may have been a gravestone in an Egyptian cemetery. The youth holds a bunch of grapes in his right hand and a dove or bird in his left. Müller has suggested that these attributes may have been relevant to the initiation rites into the mystery cult of the Egyptian goddess Isis (Müller, 1960, pp. 267, and Wessel, in Recklinghausen, n.d., no. 511). A similar standing type is in the Brooklyn Museum (Cooney, 1961, p. 2, fig. 1), but frequently representations of the acolyte show the youth crouching or sitting in his niche (cf. Wessel, 1965, p. 99, pl. 3). While it is possible that this could represent an acolyte of a pagan cult, it is also possible that the grapes symbolize the wine of the Eucharist, that the dove is either a symbol of the soul or is a sacrificial bird, which poor people used to offer instead of the lamb, which they could not afford, and that the acolyte is Christian rather than pagan. Obvious Christian symbolism occurs on a similar stele in which the youth holds a cross (Wessel, 1965, p. 76). Whether pagan or Christian, this powerful image of a provincial folk art believed to be from the region of the Middle Nile reflects the type of images which served both the ancient beliefs and those of the particular form of Christianity, the Coptic Church, which the Egyptians embraced in the fourth century A.D.

Exhibition: André Emmerich, 1962, no. 7.
Literature: Denver, n.d., p. 9.

6   STONE RELIEF: ECCLESIA REWARDING ST. BASILIDES?*
    Egypt, Coptic, 4th–5th century
    Limestone, 9 x 17 in.
    Lent by The Art Museum, Princeton University (62.46)

The Coptic relief from Princeton is one of the most enigmatic of the recently discovered sculptures believed to have been found at Sheik Ibada. It has been said that it represents the judgment of Paris or Thetis bringing armor to Achilles, both themes from classical mythology, but more recently Turnure has shown quite convincingly that the relief may represent the just award in heaven accorded to an early Christian soldier-martyr. According to Turnure, the scene depicts the kneeling Roman soldier, Basilides, who has just been converted and martyred, about to receive a shield incised with a wreath and emblazoned with a cross signifying an association of the wreath-crown accorded to martyrs with the eternal protection of the Church. The woman handing the shield to Basilides is thought to be the personification of Ecclesia, while the lady apparently interceding on the soldier's behalf may be Potómiaena, a saint who was responsible for Basilides' conversion after he had treated her with consideration on her way to her own martyrdom. The woman at the far right is then probably Potomiaena's mother, Marcella, who was martyred along with her daughter. The heavenly context of the setting is further reinforced by the presence of palm trees enframing the relief, both as symbols of the garden of paradise and perhaps also as symbols of victory—of Basilides in his martyrdom and of the Church as well.

Stylistically, the vigorous carving, the boldly projecting figures, and the parallel ropelike drapery folds relate this piece to a plaque of Christ flanked by two peacocks (Cooney, 1962, p. 53) also said to be from Sheik Ibada.

Exhibition: André Emmerich Gallery, 1962 (not illustrated).
Literature: Cooney, 1962, pp. 50, 53; Jones, 1962, pp. 53–55, fig. 14; Turnure, 1963, pp. 45–57.

7   STONE RELIEF: MARTYRDOM OF ST. STEPHEN?
     Coptic, 6th–7th century
     Limestone, 9 x 12 in.
     Lent by the William Hayes Ackland Memorial Art Center,
     University of North Carolina, Chapel Hill

More schematic and frontal than the previous Coptic relief (No. 6), this plaque presents another scene of martyrdom, perhaps of St. Stephen, in a stylized and monumental manner. Two assailants holding rocks bend sideways toward the starkly symmetrical form of their victim in the center of the composition as though they were heraldic beasts bowing before the sign of the cross. Yet there is an implication of violence as each tormentor wrenches the martyr's arm down or to the side, contrasting even more effectively with his complete imperturbability. In the slashing chevronlike folds of the garments, the radial pattern of the assailants' hair, and the trace of drill work in the hair of St. Stephen, this piece bears some resemblance to two reliefs in the Ikonen Museum in Recklinghausen, one of the Ascension and the other of the busts of two women flanking a cross possibly from Sheik Ibada (Wessel, 1965, pls. 49, 90).

Literature: Art Quarterly, XXV (1962), 71, illus.; Chapel Hill, 1962, p. 8, no. 38, illus. p. 53.

8   FRAGMENT FROM A SARCOPHAGUS?: DOLPHIN
     Early Christian or Byzantine?, 6th century
     Marble, 13¹/₄ x 8 in.
     Lent by the University of Kansas Museum of Art

Since the earliest times of Christianity the fish has served as a symbol of
the faithful, for in Greek the word *ichtys* contains the initials of Jesus
Christ Son of God, Savior. Originally used as a sign of recognition between
Christians during the first centuries of persecution, it soon became a frequently repeated symbol in the wall paintings of the catacombs and on
sarcophagi. In the present relief the fish appears in the guise of a dolphin.
Together with the presence of an anchor in the upper left corner connoting
the cross of the Crucifixion (Timmers, 1947, no. 536), the fish may then be
taken for a symbol of the Christian soul achieving salvation through the
example and sacrifice of Christ. A further implication may be imparted to
the dolphin by the pagan belief that the dolphin carried the souls of the
dead to the other world.

Beneath the dolphin is the monogram of Christ contained within a circle
in which are the Greek letters Chi and Ro, the first two letters of the word
"Christos." To this have been added the Alpha and Omega, the first and
last letters of the Greek alphabet, referring to Christ's assertion that "I am
the beginning and the end."

A relief in the Louvre (no. MA 3034) of a fish and a cross from a Coptic
cemetery of the fourth to fifth century A.D. (Coche de la Ferté, 1958, no. 7,
pp. 14, 88) carries many of the same implications as the dolphin relief, and
suggests that the Kansas plaque may have come from a funerary monument,
perhaps a sarcophagus.

Exhibition: Tulsa, 1965, no. 3.

9   DECORATIVE BANDS FROM A TUNIC
     Egypt, Coptic, 5th–6th century
     Linen and wool roundels, diameter 6¹/₈ in.; clavii, length 25¹/₂ in.;
     sleeve bands, length 12³/₄ in.
     Lent by The Art Museum, Princeton University (48.25)

Woven decorative panels frequently adorned the tunics worn by the peoples
of the Late Antique period. The *clavii* were long strips, in this case terminating in roundels, flanking the neck opening. The two shorter, broader
sleeve bands and the four roundels, probably placed between the *clavii* and
the hem of the garment, completed the decoration.

The subject matter of these brilliantly colored, decorative textile fragments has not been positively identified. In the roundels, a blond-headed
and seminude male figure is seated on a stool or throne, holding an object
that looks like a torch in his right hand and reaching into a fruit basket
with his left. A standing figure holding a staff or a spear occupies the central
field of the *clavii*, while again figures holding two birds appear between two

trees in the end sections. The shoulder bands seem to combine these motifs: a seated figure appears in the central medallion and the birdcatcher and soldier standing amid trees occur in the fields on each side. The borders of all the decorative panels consist of a zigzag and foliate motif.

Former Collection: Vladimir G. Simkhovitch.
Exhibitions: The Century Club, 1930; Avery Library, 1931; Brooklyn, 1941, no. 218; Baltimore, 1947, no. 788.
Literature: Record of the Art Museum, Princeton University, VII, no. 2, (1948), 11; Jones and Goldberg, 1960, pp. 70–71.

10   SQUARE TEXTILE PANEL: ORPHEUS
Egypt, Coptic, 5th century
Linen, $6^{1}/_{2}$ in. sq.
Lent by The Art Museum, Princeton University (52.76)

Sometimes a square panel of linen tapestry was placed near the hem of a garment instead of the roundels used in No. 9 above. In this example, a round medallion flanked by a dragon in each corner is set within the square frame. In the center, Orpheus plays his lyre while two satyrs and a number of animals dance. Here, as perhaps in the previous example of Coptic textile, we have a continuing use of pagan themes and bucolic scenes in the ornamentation of secular garments, at a time when the Coptic branch of the Christian Church was growing in Egypt.

Exhibition: Baltimore, 1947, no. 806.

11   IVORY PLAQUE: CRUCIFIXION*
Byzantine, 10th century
Ivory, $3^{3}/_{8}$ x $5^{1}/_{4}$ in.
Lent by The Art Museum, Princeton University (42.60)

The strong and moving image of Christ on the Cross placed between the ruggedly carved figures of the mourning Virgin and St. John and flanked by the sun and moon represents an important transition in the dogma of the Byzantine Church and its iconographical reflection in cult images. The body of Christ in the Princeton ivory is shown almost erect, but with a trace of contrapposto and of a slightly swaying axis, while the head is slightly inclined to the left and the eyes are apparently closed. In the erect posture there is still the influence of the earlier type of living and triumphant Christ on the Cross that was in vogue during the early Byzantine period and in Europe during the Carolingian era. But the earlier form is now combined with a new implication that this is the dead and suffering Christ, the symbol of the ultimate sacrifice for the ultimate salvation of mankind. The iconography of the dead Christ has been shown to reflect the anti-iconoclastic polemical writings of Nicephorus, patriarch of Constantinople (805–815), who not only sought to revive the practice of representing Christ, but also stressed the implications of Christ's death upon the Cross (Martin, 1955, pp. 193–194). The customary representation of the crucifix in the tenth century was that of the still hieratic and stiff image of the dead Christ as exemplified by the Princeton plaque. Later, the figure of Christ would adopt a more emphatic S-shaped curve accentuating the emotional and agonizing espects of the Crucifixion, as in the mosaic at Daphne, c.1100.

Stylistically, the Princeton plaque is related to a group of ivories similar to an ivory in Cortona that contains an inscription referring to Emperor Nicephorus Phocas (963–969) and hence nicknamed the "Nicephorus group" (Goldschmidt and Weitzmann, 1934, II, 18–20).

Former Collection: Count Wilczek, Kreuzenstein, Lower Austria.
Exhibitions: Dresden, 1906, no. 1413; Baltimore, 1947, no. 132, pl. XXVII.
Literature: Record of the Art Museum, Princeton University, XIII, no. 1 (1954), p. 6; Goldschmidt and Weitzmann, 1934, II, 56, no. 103, pl. XL; Friend, 1942, pp. 9–10.

12   IVORY PLAQUE: CRUCIFIXION
      Byzantine, 10th century
      Ivory, $5^1/_4$ x 4 3/16 in.
      Lent by the Walters Art Gallery, Baltimore (71.113)

As in the Princeton plaque above (No. 11), the figure of the dead Christ is represented between the figures of the Virgin and St. John. In this case, however, a stronger emotive device is combined with a more emphatic hieratic quality of the figure. The tilt of Christ's head is accentuated to reinforce the idea of suffering and death, but the eyes are open, and the body is more rigidly frontal and erect than in the Princeton example, thus remaining closer to the earlier type of the Christ Triumphant on the Cross discussed above. The position of the Virgin turned toward Christ remains the same as in the Princeton plaque, but now the figure of St. John also turns to make a gesture of grief in the direction of the crucified form. The scene is enframed by an architectural motif, an arcade of acroterialike forms supported by spirally fluted Corinthian columns and terminated by palmettes on the corners. The particular form of this arcade is one of a number of frequently repeated variations of an architectural frame, which in its more elaborate form represents a baldachino. In form and style, the Baltimore relief closely resembles an ivory of the Crucifixion set into the bookcover of the Bernward Evangeliary in the Cathedral Treasury at Hildesheim (Goldschmidt and Weitzmann, 1934, Vol. II, no. 106, pl. XL, pp. 18–20), which Goldschmidt also places in the "Nicephorus group."

Exhibition: Baltimore, 1947, no. 133, pl. XXVI.

13   IVORY PLAQUE: DEPOSITION*
      Italo-Byzantine, 12th century
      Ivory, $6^1/_4$ x $4^1/_2$ in.
      Lent by the Museum of Fine Arts, Boston (34.1462)

The representation of the Deposition of Christ from the Cross manifests still a greater attention to the theme of the martyrdom of Christ. Here, Joseph of Arimathea is shown perched on a stepladder gently lowering the emaciated and wracked body of Christ into the outstretched arms of the Virgin. A helper draws the nails from Christ's feet, while St. John stands on a nearby hillock lamenting and half figures of weeping angels hover above. Probably from a triptych, the plaque is remarkable for the spatial quality imparted to it by the deep undercutting of the forms, some portions of which are completely detached from the background. This plaque is usually accepted as an Italian copy of a Byzantine plaque or even of an almost identical ivory relief of the eleventh century in the Cathedral Treasury at Hildesheim (Goldschmidt and Weitzmann, 1934, II, 78, nos. 219, 220, pl. LXX). The treatment and style are considered to reflect early thirteenth-century Tuscan or north Italian art (*ibid.* and Hipkiss, 1935).

Former Collection: Trivulzio Collection, Milan.
Exhibition: Milan, 1874, no. 7; Baltimore, 1947, no. 138.
Literature: Courajod, 1875, p. 377; Goldschmidt and Weitzmann, 1934, II, 78, no. 220, pl. LXX; Hipkiss, 1935.

14   RELIQUARY CROSS
       Asia Minor or Egypt, 6th–7th century
       Bronze, set with green stone, $4^1/_4$ x 2 in.
       Lent by the Newark Museum (50.2276)
       The Mrs. Robert E. deForest Collection of Crosses. Gift of her daughters, 1950

Made of two flat cross-shaped bronze plaques and hinged at the top, this cross may have been created to contain relics obtained by pilgrims from Asia Minor or Egypt to the Holy Land in the sixth or seventh centuries A.D. (King and Morey, 1928). The front is decorated with an incised, stylized figure with hands upraised. Figures in this *orans* posture, or posture of prayer, were often represented in devotional images during the Early Christian period. They occur frequently in the catacomb paintings in Rome (e.g., the Catacomb of St. Priscilla) and are engraved or embossed on numerous other crosses of this type (Baltimore, 1947, nos. 295–307, especially no. 302 from Detroit, no. 26.73,74). The back is decorated with an incised star-shaped design punctuated by concentric circles at the points and angles and set with a green stone in the center.

Exhibitions: Tulsa, 1965, no. 18; Wheaton College, 1965.
Literature: Dusenbury, 1960, pp. 4–5.

15   HALF OF A BRONZE RELIQUARY CROSS
       Byzantine, Syro-Palestinian, 6th–7th century
       Bronze, 4 15/16 x $3^1/_8$ in.
       Lent by the Detroit Institute of Arts (26.57)

A slightly later and more elaborately decorated form of reliquary cross than No. 14 is exemplified by this example from Detroit. The central portion is adorned by a relief of the Virgin and Child, and the flaring arms contain relief medallions with the busts of the four Evangelists, who are identified by vertical inscriptions. Although considerably worn, it is evident that the relief was modeled in an accomplished manner and that the forms have lost some of the crudeness of conception and hieratic stiffness evident in the Newark cross. This image is similar in form to that contained on the reverse of a reliquary cross in the Vatican (King and Morey, 1928, pp. 198ff. and pl. XXIV, fig. 1).

Exhibition: Baltimore, 1947, no. 305.
Literature: Eastman, 1926, pp. 95–96.

16   ENAMEL PLAQUE: BAPTISM OF CHRIST†
Byzantine, 12th century
Cloisonné enamel on gold, 5 1/16 x 4 5/16 in.
Lent by the Detroit Institute of Arts (39.674)
Gift of Robert H. Tannahill

One of the most resplendent of all the arts of the Byzantine Empire was that of producing cloisonné enamel plaques. In the sheer brilliance of the colors, the glitter of the gold background, and the striking contrasts of the patterns, the enamel plaques rivaled on a small scale the shimmering mosaics adorning Byzantine churches and perhaps inspired miniaturists to invoke the same effects in their jewellike illustrations of manuscripts (see No. 18 below). In the plaque of the *Baptism of Christ*, Christ is shown immersed almost up to his shoulders in the blue waters of the Jordan, while St. John the Baptist on the left pours water over His head and three attendant angels on the right hold His garments. Four fish are shown swimming in the river, olive branches in the foreground suggest vegetation, and the dark blue banks of the river lead back to the boulderlike hills silhouetted against the shimmering gold sky. The white silhouette of the Dove of the Holy Ghost descends upon a red ray emanating from the concentric blue circles of Heaven above as Christ makes a gesture of benediction. At the same time the ultimate triumph over Evil is symbolized by Christ's treading on a serpent.

The Baptism plaque is one of eleven (perhaps originally twelve) plaques that were in the collection of Prince M. P. Botkin in St. Petersburg until the early part of the twentieth century. Another plaque from this group, representing the Transfiguration, is also in Detroit, and four others representing the Ascension, the Deësis, the Crucifixion, and the Presentation of Christ at the Temple are in the Metropolitan Museum in New York (see Siple, 1928, and Rorimer, 1938). Presumably these plaques represented the twelve feasts of the Church and may have adorned a portable iconostasis, or screen, used to separate the sanctuary of a Byzantine church from the nave (Weibel, 1928, p. 93). Not all of these, however, are identical in style or format, and some have been considered to be later in date than the twelfth century. The Detroit *Baptism* is one of the finest plaques of the group and fully exemplifies the nature of this spectacular art.

The technique of cloisonné enamel is one of the oldest in metalwork. The main outlines of the design and the interior articulating lines of the forms are created by thin ridges of gold wire. These act as divisions between the areas of the patterns, and when the plaque is fired, they separate the pools of molten glass. In the Detroit *Baptism*, the pure translucent quality of the colors and the bold patterning of the cells forming the landscape are effectively contrasted with the rhythmic undulation of a myriad of gold lines in the ripples of the river and the concentric linear folds in the draperies.

Former Collection: M. P. Botkin, St. Petersburg.
Exhibitions: Hartford, 1948, no. 35; Cooper Union, 1954, no. 18; Buffalo, 1964, no. 43.
Literature: Botkin, 1911, pl. 88; Weibel, 1928, pp. 90–93; Siple, 1928, pp. 197–199; Gnau, 1955, p. 37.

17   MEDALLION: ST. MARK*
     Byzantine, 12th century
     Cloisonné enamel on gold, diameter $3^1/_8$ in.
     Lent by The Art Museum, Princeton University (48.12)

Cloisonné enamel medallions, as well as rectangular plaques (No. 16), were often used as decoration for altar frontals, iconostases, or frames of icons. Nine enamel medallions similar to the one from Princeton, which originally adorned the Monastery at Djumati, Georgia, are now preserved in the Metropolitan Museum of Art (Rorimer, 1938, fig. 1).

In the Princeton example the bold and simplified bust of the Evangelist is presented as though slightly turning to his right. He points with his right hand to a bound copy of the Gospels with heart-shaped designs on the cover, which he holds in his left. The implication would be the same here as one frequently finds in representations of the Virgin and Child of the Hodegetria type, where the Virgin is gesturing toward the Child held in the crook of her arm or seated on her lap. In both cases the attention is being directed to the figure of Christ, or to the example of His ministry as contained in the Gospels, to remind the beholder that this is the way, through the words and deeds of Christ, to salvation.

Freely meandering lines created by the gold wire defining the cloisons give the drapery a more rumpled appearance than the intense striations of the previous example.

Former Collection: M. P. Botkin, St. Petersburg.
Literature: Botkin, 1911, pl. 84; *Record of the Art Museum, Princeton University*, VII, no. 2 (1948), 11.

18   FOLIO FROM A PSALTER: MINIATURE OF MOSES
     RECEIVING THE LAW
     Byzantine, *c.*1088
     Tempera and gold leaf on vellum, $4^5/_8$ x $3^5/_8$ in.
     Lent by the Walters Art Gallery, Baltimore (MS. W.530 B)

The jewellike miniature representing Moses receiving the Ten Commandments employs a narrative device that one frequently encounters in medieval art. Moses is depicted, not once, but three times in a string of events surrounding his experience on Mount Sinai. On the upper left side of the miniature, Moses is shown removing his sandals, obeying God's command when he turned aside to have a better look at the burning bush (Exodus III, 2: "Do not come near; put off your shoes from your feet, for the place on which you are standing is holy ground"). On the upper right, Moses is climbing and reaching upward to receive the tablets of the Law from the hand of God, appearing out of an arc of blue cloud. At the bottom of the miniature, Moses is shown addressing the elders and handing them a scroll with the Ten Commandments. Three separate incidents are thus represented simultaneously, each contained in an implied pocket of space, but at the same time unified by the continuity of the landscape and the repetitive color pattern of Moses' garments.

Weitzmann (1947) has shown that the Baltimore page comes from a Byzantine Psalter at Mount Athos (Vatopedi Monastery, MS. 761) and that this folio and the remaining miniatures in the volume occupy a unique place in the development of illustrative cycles in Greek psalters. The particular combination of motifs and events in the Baltimore page, as well as in the other similar miniatures in Vatopedi 761 (the manuscript also contains four later and cruder miniatures) depicting the Crossing of the Red Sea and scenes from the Life of David, appears to be close in iconography and composition to a lost archetype that established this distinctive cycle of psalter illustration known as the Aristocratic Recension. In this case the production of the manuscript in the provinces and by an uninventive artist who preferred to copy rather than elaborate has preserved for us an intriguing link with the origins of an iconographical cycle. Although the artist and the exact place of production of the Vatopedi manuscript may never be known, the presence of Easter tables for the years 1088 to 1111 suggest that the manuscript was written and illuminated toward the beginning of that period, or about 1088.

Former Collection: Mount Athos, Vatopedi Monastery.
Exhibitions: Baltimore, 1947, no. 699; Oberlin, 1957, no. 1.
Literature: de Ricci, 1935, I, 826, no. 415; Clark, 1937, p. 360; Weitzmann, 1947.

19   FOLIO FROM GOSPELS: MINIATURE OF ST. MATTHEW*
     Byzantine, 12th century
     Tempera and gold leaf on vellum, 9 x 6 in.
     Lent by the Walters Art Gallery, Baltimore (MS. W.530E)

It became the custom in both eastern and western medieval manuscripts of the New Testament to introduce each of the Gospels with a portrait of the respective Evangelist. It is possible that this tradition goes back to Late Antique representations of philosophers, authors, or poets and was, like so many other classical motifs, adapted to the Christian context.

The figure of St. Matthew is situated in an implied interior against a shimmering gold background. The throne and cushion upon which he sits, the footrest beneath his feet, and the combination cabinet-desk and lectern upon which he writes are often-repeated props in the Evangelist portraits. The implication of an architectural setting is further reinforced by the presence of a tower behind the Saint's throne. In this miniature the rumpled, activated drapery, the intentness of gesture as the Evangelist reaches forward to dip his pen, and the concentration of his expression created by the accentuated modeling of his face effectively imply that the Saint is caught up in the moment of inspiration. These same qualities, together with the almost identical repetition of the form of the lectern with a scroll draped across it, relate this miniature to one in a Byzantine gospel book in London (British Museum, MS. Burney 19, fol. lv: Athens, 1964, no. 314) and in turn to a group of manuscripts produced in a scriptoria in Constantinople, one of which (Vatican Library, MS. Urb. 2) is dated 1128–1129. The brilliant coloring and the use of a shimmering gold background reflect the radiant quality of cloisonné enamels such as Nos. 16 and 17 above.

Exhibitions: Baltimore, 1947, no. 718; Oberlin, 1957, no. 9.
Literature: de Ricci, 1935, I, 826, no. 415; Clark, 1937, p. 361.

20   BOW FIBULA
     Ostrogothic, *c.*500–550
     Gilt bronze set with semiprecious stones, $8^7/8$ x $2^5/8$ in.
     Lent by the Detroit Institute of Arts (26.159)

Probably worn as a pin to fasten garments together at the shoulder, this fibula typifies the art of the wandering barbarian tribes throughout Europe during the decline of the Roman Empire. It has been shown to be one of the most elaborate surviving examples of Ostrogothic metalwork, being most similar to other fibulae transported into Italy by the Ostrogoths in the sixth century A.D. (Kühn, 1938, p. 270).

The pin is bow-shaped in the middle with a semicircular "digitated" head plate and a rhomboid-shaped foot plate. Seven projecting animal-headed tabs interspersed with stylized bird-head ornaments are adorned with seven red cabochon gems, possibly garnets. Four similar tabs project from the foot plate, which is decorated with five cabochon gems. Three parallel animal-headed tabs complete the foot of the fibula. The entire surface is covered by concentric framing borders and curvilinear incised ornament. The fusion of geometric forms and patterns with curvilinear motifs and animal forms reflects a sophisticated level of decorative achievement in a period when the principal art forms seem to have been easily portable articles of personal jewelry and precious objects manufactured for burial raiments.

Former Collection: Luigi Grassi, Florence.
Exhibitions: Baltimore, 1947, no. 847.
Literature: Kühn, 1938.

21 BOW FIBULA*
Merovingian, 5th–6th century
Silver gilt inlaid with niello and paste, 3 5/16 x 1 13/16 in.
Lent by the City Art Museum of St. Louis (57.49)

A more simple form of the digitated bow fibula than the Ostrogothic pin from Detroit (No. 20), the St. Louis example combines a semicircular head plate with five projecting tabs set with garnets and a triangular foot plate terminating in a stylized animal mask. The incised linear decoration on the surface of the pin reflects the geometrical form of each basic element of the pin, rather than consisting of the free scrollwork of the Ostrogothic fibula. The semicircular head plate is subdivided into three triangular areas and the median ridge running along the bow is punctuated with a series of nielloed circles. Except for some variation in form, the general arrangement and decoration are similar to a Frankish fibula in the Walters Art Gallery said to date from about 600 (no. 54.2443; Ross, 1961, no. 24). The St. Louis fibula represents a common type produced in the region of northeastern France and the Rhine Valley during the Merovingian period.

Literature: Bulletin of the City Art Museum of St. Louis, Spring 1950, pp. 4–5.

22 BRONZE BUCKLE*
Merovingian, 7th century
Bronze, 7 x 3 1/16 in.
Lent by the Worcester Art Museum (1949.21)

The massive bronze buckle, overlaid with silver, decorated with incised interlace designs, and punctuated by seven large bosses riveted to the edge of the belt plate, is typical of a type produced by the Frankish tribes in southwestern France, in the region of Aquitaine. The belt plate is divided into three panels of interlace decoration, the central one containing a lozenge-shaped frame with a zoomorphic design of a continuous snakelike two-headed bird. The center bands of the interlace ribbons and the ground are textured with stippling.

In format, in dimensions, and particularly in the configurations of the interwoven decoration, the Worcester buckle is practically identical with a buckle in the Walters Art Gallery (no. 54.2350; Ross, 1961, no. 30). This striking similarity led to the discovery that both buckles were found at the same site, at the cemetery of Tabariane at Teilhet (Ariège), and that the Worcester buckle was published and illustrated by Roger in 1908 (Roger, 1908, pp. 318–319, pl. XX, no. 3). Both buckles passed into the Brummer collection, and the Walters buckle (no. 871 C) may have been the one similar to the Worcester buckle (no. 871 B) exhibited at the Early Christian and Byzantine Exhibition in 1947.

Former Collections: de Lorey Collection; Brummer Collection.
Exhibitions: Worcester, 1937, no. 116; Baltimore, 1947, no. 871 B; Tulsa, 1965, no. 46.

Literature: Roger, 1908, pp. 318–319, pl. XX, no. 3; Brummer, 1949, I, 55–56, no. 232; Worcester Art Museum, *News Bulletin and Calendar*, XV, no. 1 (Oct. 1949), 1–2; Worcester Art Museum, *Annual Report*, 1950, p. xii.

23 FOLIO FROM GOSPELS: TITLE PAGES OF GOSPELS
ACCORDING TO ST. JOHN*
German, Corvey?, *c.*950–975
Tempera and gold on vellum, $12^{1}/_{4}$ x $9^{1}/_{2}$ in., 4 folios
Lent by the Walters Art Gallery, Baltimore (MS. W.751)

Many diverse elements can be seen coming together in the splendid decorative pages of this fragment from a gospel book of the early Ottonian period. The four folios containing a frontispiece and a decorative incipit page for each of the Gospels of St. Luke and St. John were probably taken from a manuscript in the Bibliothèque Municipale at Reims (MS. 10; Reims, 1967, no. 5, and Mütherich, 1963, pp. 32–34) that is generally considered to have been produced at the Abbey of Corvey in the Weser Valley.

The elaborate frontispiece to the Gospels of St. John, containing the words "Inicium Sci Euangelii Secundum Johannem" in gold letters against a purple ground, is dominated by a cross pattern in the center, four roundels with stylized birds in the interstices, and a frame with corner medallions containing heraldic beasts surrounding the design. Both the frame and cross are made up of panels with a continuous interlace pattern, and the central medallion of the cross is filled with a foliate motif. The "incipit page," or opening page, of the Gospels of St. John is framed by a similar border, but contains the words "In Principio" almost disguised in intricate interlace designs and interwoven foliate tendrils.

The use of a gold text set against a purple ground of dyed vellum dates back to Early Christian times, to manuscripts that were produced for the imperial court. The revival of this imperial format and iconography can be seen in numerous manuscripts produced for the Carolingian and Ottonian courts. In the Baltimore-Reims manuscript, this tradition is fused with several others. The cruciform frontispiece to St. John continues the practice found in manuscripts produced in the British Isles of prefacing an incipit page with a "carpet page" of abstract but usually cruciform pattern filled with a myriad of tightly woven zoomorphic forms and interlaced ribbons. Here, the format is combined with roundels and medallions containing birds and animals, which have the heraldic quality of both barbarian metalwork (cf. the Sutton Hoo purse lid) and Byzantine textiles. In the outlining of the colored areas by gold lines, there is a reflection of the effects of cloisonné enamel, which one suspects is intentional. The purely decorative treatment of the incipit page also reflects a tradition stemming from Anglo-Irish manuscript illumination (cf. the Chi-Ro page of the Book of Kells), where the letters are very difficult to decipher, but in this case the elaborate foliate decoration mirrors developments in illumination around the Abbey of Corvey in the latter tenth century. The almost illegible opening phrases, however, would not have daunted the monks who read this book, for they would have known the opening lines from memory. The Baltimore pages, therefore, represent an important link between the purely decorative traditions of the pre-Carolingian and so-called "Franco-Saxon" manuscript illumination of the latter ninth century and the early Ottonian style at Corvey as manifested by the Wernigerode Gospels in the Morgan Library (MS. 755: Grabar and Nordenfalk, 1957, p. 196, for color illustration, and Harrsen, 1958, p. 13).

Former Collections: Chapter Library, Cathedral of Notre Dame, Reims (before the French Revolution); Sir Thomas Philipps, MS. 14122; A. Chester Beatty, MS. 10 (1921–1952).
Exhibitions: Pierpont Morgan Library, 1934, no. 11; Los Angeles, 1953, no. 1; Queens College, 1959, no. 82; The Grolier Club, 1962; Berkeley, 1963, no. 1, pls. II, III; Cleveland, 1964, no. 1; Tulsa, 1965, no. 49; Corvey, 1966, no. 164.
Literature: Millar, 1927, I, 48–49, no. 10, pls. XXVI–XXVII; Boeckler, 1930, p. 51; Tikkanen, 1933, p. 299; Schardt, 1938, pp. 58–61; Miner, 1952, pp. 1–3, 4; Harrsen, 1958, p. 13; Diringer, 1958, p. 183, pl. III–25b (*idem*, 1967, p. 224, pl. IV–25); Bond, 1962, p. 198, no. 567; Mütherich, 1963, pp. 32–34; Reims, 1967, p. 15.

24   LION*
German, *c.*1050
Bronze, $5^5/_8$ x $4^7/_8$ in.
Lent by the Rhode Island School of Design, Museum of Art (64.039)

The vivacious and ferocious little lion, crouched as though about to spring and turning its head to roar, was probably a support for some object, as evidenced by the hole in the lower part of the back. In the eyes of medieval people, clerics and lay persons alike, the lion was well suited to this task:

Leo the Lion, mightiest of beasts will stand up to anybody. . . . When he sleeps, he seems to keep his eyes open. . . . What creature dares declare himself an enemy to this beast, in whose roar there is such natural terribleness that many animals, which could escape its charge by their speed, fail to get away from the very sound of its voice—as if dumbfounded and overcome by brute force! (White, 1960, pp. 7–11)

So reads a twelfth-century account in a bestiary (Cambridge, University Library, MS. II, 4.26), a book of natural history which sought to explain the habits of various animals and to relate them to the scriptures. Thus, in addition to being the symbol of St. Mark, the lion was seen as a faithful and courageous watchdog of the Church. It is in this role that we frequently find a pair of reclining but alert lions patiently supporting the columns of porches sheltering the portals of Romanesque churches (e.g., San Zeno, Verona). A similar significance may be imparted to the great lions' heads that served as knockers or handles on Romanesque bronze doors (e.g., at Hildesheim and Durham) and as supports for candlesticks or baptismal fonts (see Falke and Meyer, 1935, nos. 437–439, pls. 182–183). Later, notably in the fourteenth century, lions were used as vessels, known as aquamaniles, for pouring holy water (see No. 69).

The Providence Lion appears to be a fairly early example of the guardian supporting lion. The simple, smoothly flowing volumes of the body, the emphasis on the widely opened circular eyes with slitted pupils and on the sharply pointed triangular teeth, and the decorative quality of the scroll-like clumps of mane relate this piece to the powerfully abstracted animal forms found in barbarian and Anglo-Irish art of the eighth and ninth centuries. The prancing, heraldic Lion of St. Mark in the Echternach Gospels of about 690 (Paris, Bibliothèque Nationale, MS. lat. 9389) has aptly been compared with the Providence beast (Glass, 1965, p. 1). Glass quite justifiably equates the spirit of the crouching lion to the intensely ferocious and stylized lion-head door knockers at Hildesheim of about 1015 and suggests that the Providence example may date from slightly later, about 1050.

Literature: College Art Journal, XXIV, no. 2 (winter 1964/65), 162, fig. 2; Glass, 1965, pp. 1–13.

25   FOLIO FROM A SACRAMENTARY*
      Southern Italian, Benevento, *c.*1100
      Vellum, 14$^{1}/_{2}$ x 10 1/16 in.
      Lent by the Lansburgh–Colorado College Collection, Colorado Springs

One of the most important monastic foundations of the early Middle Ages was the Benedictine monastery at Monte Cassino, about midway between Rome and Naples. It was here that an influential and prolific scriptorium flourished in the latter part of the tenth and beginning of the eleventh centuries. The peculiar script that evolved primarily at Monte Cassino soon pervaded all the scriptoria of southern Italy and is known as "Beneventan" after the ancient duchy that comprised most of the area. In addition to the distinctive paleography, which has been studied at length by E. A. Lowe (1914), there developed a style of zoomorphic and foliate interlace initials which arose out of the barbarian and insular traditions of interlace patterns and lacertines and which were, in turn, the precursors of the inhabited initials of the Romanesque period (see Nos. 26 and 27).

The Lansburgh–Colorado College page, containing the openings of two readings on I Peter V, 6, and Mark II, 13, from a Sacramentary, was found in the binding of a manuscript. The vigorously penned initials are made of ribbonlike forms, which double back and loop through themselves. Sprouting tendrils and circular nodules with dots in the centers, the initials terminate in dragon heads, which turn back to bite their own bodies. Inasmuch as the illumination of initials in the latter third of the eleventh century at the Monte Cassino scriptorium seems to have been influenced by the dense patterning of Ottonian manuscripts (see Lowe, 1929, Vol. II, pls. LXVII and LXVIII; see also No. 23 above), the Lansburgh–Colorado Springs page appears to have been produced elsewhere. Its initials reflect a style that prevailed in the more provincial regions of the Benevento and most closely resemble those found in a manuscript of 1145 from near Troja (Naples, Biblioteca Nazionale, MS. VI. B. 3: Lowe, 1929, Vol. II, pl. LXXXVII). On the basis of this similarity, a localization of this page to the southern portion of the duchy of Benevento seems possible.

26   FOLIO FROM *DECRETALS* OF GRATIANUS: INITIAL *Q**
      Eastern French or German, 12th century
      Tempera on vellum, $13^1/_2$ x $6^3/_8$ in.
      Lent by The Art Museum, Princeton University (1029)

The development seen in the initial *Q* on this folio from a copy of the *Decretals* of Gratianus reflects the trend found in most Romanesque manuscripts. In the Princeton page, the structure of the initial is boldly stated by a double framework, a kind of trellis upon which climb two different-colored interlaced tendrils. A sprawling dragon forms the tail of the latter, its head devouring the lower clump of foliate decoration, its tail turning into a pinwheel of four sprouting fleshy leaves. The entire initial is set off against the page by an irregular colored ground. This initial is therefore no longer the zoomorphic interlace from which the Beneventan initials seem to derive, but is rather a reflection of a new type, the inhabited initial in which birds, animals, and sometimes human figures climb about and become entangled in the decorative undergrowth.

The subtle pastel shades and matt quality of the pigments are distinctive features of this initial and seem to have an affinity with northeastern French illumination of the first half of the twelfth century. It has been observed that some pages from a similar manuscript from eastern France preserved in the Victoria and Albert Museum (nos. 8985 B–F: Victoria and Albert Museum, 1908, II, 65, nos. 688–93, and 1923, p. 57) were from the same book; however, the five initials in London are somewhat different in execution, while the paleography and ruling of the columns are all at variance with the Princeton page. Yet they are similar enough in style to ascribe them to the same general locale and period.

27   CUT-OUT INITIAL *O*
      English, 12th century
      Gold and tempera on vellum, 5 x $3^7/_8$ in.
      Lent by The Art Museum, Princeton University (1026)

Further elaboration of the inhabited type of initial can be seen in this cut-out initial from Princeton. The basic structure of the letter is almost lost in the entanglement of foliate tendrils, which terminate in biting animal heads or large, unbudding leaf forms. One of the tendrils loops above the initial and turns into a convoluted dragon, which attacks a stoatlike animal caught in the curving shape of its body. A smaller but similar animal in the center of

117

the initial attacks the neck of another dragon, who in turn bites into a foliate stem. Below, two other animals bite into curving tendrils. Throughout, the emphasis is on a primeval ferociousness of constantly biting forms, a tendency which stems from the barbarian tradition of northern Europe some four or five centuries before and which in the Romanesque period pervaded illuminated initials and carved architectural decoration such as capitals surmounting the columns of churches and cloisters.

The strong, brilliant colors and the clarity and precision of the decorative scheme is reminiscent of the effect achieved by the early masters who worked on the Winchester Bible in England in the middle of the twelfth century (see Oakshott, 1945).

28   BIBLE (INCOMPLETE)*
      English, Winchester, c.1145
      Tempera on vellum, 174 leaves, 16$^3/_4$ x 13 in.
      Text in 2 columns of 40 lines
      Lent by the Pierpont Morgan Library, New York (MS. M. 823)

Illuminated manuscripts filled the libraries of monasteries and clerics in the Middle Ages, but some were destined to remain in the pulpits of churches, and others, including the present English bible, were intended to remain on the lecterns of refectories to be read aloud from during meals (Wormald, 1958, p. 29, n. 9). This volume contains portions of the Bible in Latin, parts of Genesis, Exodus, Leviticus, Numbers, Deuteronomy, Joshua, Judges, Jeremiah, Acts, Epistles, and Apocalypse, but does not contain the four Gospels. There are five large illuminated initials, some smaller decorative ones, and numerous ornamental initials in blue and green.

The initial *L* introducing the Book of Numbers is fully within the Romanesque tradition, as we have observed above (Nos. 26–27). The letter consists of a trellislike structure, heavily entwined by interlacing bands of red and blue foliage, contorted biting dragons, and the nude figure of a man. Since the entire introductory phrase enframed by the initial is made up of multicolored letters and was therefore painted rather than written by the scribe, the person who executed this portion of the page needed to know what to put in the space. To the right of this passage, we can still see the instructions for the rubrics written in the margin. The distinctive use of lavender and green in the larger initials and the employment of white dots along the black contours of the forms suggests a certain link with some Durham manuscripts (e.g., Durham, Cathedral Library, MS. B.II.16: Mynors, 1939, pl. 24), but there is also a prevalence of decorative initials in blue and green without outlines and with ragged palmette forms, which relate the decoration to that of the Winchester Bible.

Former Collections: Refectory of the Augustinian Priory at Taunton, England; Thomas Pawle (later 15th century); R. J. A. Arundel, Esq. (1947).
Exhibition: Vatican Pavillion, New York World's Fair, 1964.

Literature: Sotheby Catalogue, Nov. 24, 1947, pp. 9–10, lot no. 63; Pierpont Morgan Library, 1949, pp. 38–39; Wormald, 1958, p. 29, no. 9; Bond, 1962, p. 361 (M.823); Ker, 1964, pp. 188, 373.

29 MINIATURES FROM A PSALTER: BETRAYAL OF CHRIST; CHRIST BEFORE PILATE*

Southern German, Diocese of Augsburg, 13th century

Gold and tempera on vellum, 9 folios, $8^{1}/_{4}$ x $5^{1}/_{2}$ in.

19 lines of text, 7 full-page miniatures, 4 full-page historiated initials

Lent by the Pierpont Morgan Library, New York (MS. M.275)

A prolific and somewhat provincial school of illumination flourished in southern Germany in the region of Augsburg during the first half of the thirteenth century, and numerous manuscripts and fragments of them have survived in collections here and abroad (see Swarzenski, 1936, I, 59–60, 136–142, nos. 57–67, II, figs. 743–783). This group is marked by repetitiveness of the same compositions, a use of browns, blues, and reds in the garments, large-proportioned figures, and a highly burnished gold background. Usually the figures are in somewhat stiff poses, but in the present example a slight indication of the Gothic may be seen in the tendency to articulate folds of the garments and to impart expressiveness to the features by the lively expression of the eyes. These miniatures, as in most of the Augsburg productions, are framed by a series of colored bands—two tones of blue, gold, and two tones of rose.

In the *Betrayal of Christ,* Judas reaches out to embrace Christ, thereby revealing Him to the soldiers and a high priest in a tall candlelike hat who crowd in around Him. The miniature of *Christ before Pilate* is in the form of a historiated initial set in the letter *D* (*Dixit custodi*) introducing Psalm 39.

Literature: Olschki, 1908, pp. 82–83; Swarzenski, 1936, I, 59–60 (n. 1), 141 (no. 65), 164 (n. 7, M.257 should read M.275), II, figs. 749, 750, 754, 769a, 777; de Ricci, 1937, II, 1418, no. 275; Harrsen, 1958, p. 39, no. 25, pls. 43 and 44; Buddenseig, 1958, p. 244.

30 MARGINAL ILLUSTRATIONS FROM A BIBLE: CHRIST IN MAJESTY; ELKANAH AND HIS WIVES*

Northern Italian or Sicilian, *c*.1260

Gold and tempera on vellum, 5 x $2^{1}/_{4}$ in.; $3^{3}/_{4}$ x $4^{1}/_{4}$ in.

Lent by the Walters Art Gallery, Baltimore (MS. W.152A and C)

One of the most spectacular manuscripts in the collection of the Walters Art Gallery, the so-called Conradin Bible (MS. W.152), has both delighted and puzzled scholars by its bold colors, its vigorously executed miniatures, and its unique placement and format of the illustrations (see Miner, 1966, for the most recent discussion of the Bible and previous bibliography). An unsubstantiated tradition has it that the manuscript was sent from Sicily to King Conradin of Hohenstaufen in 1267–1268. The volume contains 104 of an original 120 miniatures, all of which are arranged in large irregular fields in the ample margins. Recently several of the missing cut-out miniatures from the Conradin Bible, including the two exhibited, were also acquired by the Walters Art Gallery.

The miniatures of *Christ in Majesty*, which introduced Psalm 110 (109), and Elkanah, the father of Samuel, and his wives, which introduced the Book of Samuel (I Kings), reflect all the vigor and brilliant coloring of the miniatures in the bible itself. The fields of blue and rose are articulated by large gold dots, which are bounded with black lines punctuated by white dots, and are interconnected by white filigree patterns. In the treatment of the figures there is a fusion of bold and flat patternized Romanesque forms with a reflection of Byzantine models in the treatment of the faces. The *Christ in Majesty* reflects all the severity and monumentality of the Byzantine-style Pantocrator of the apse mosaics at Palermo and Monreale in Sicily. In the miniature *Elkanah and His Wives*, however, the faces retain a more Romanesque cast, while the somewhat more loosely articulated draperies in flowing folds contain a hint of the impending Gothic.

So far no close stylistic parallel to the miniatures of the Conradin Bible has come to light, though the format of the miniatures has been linked to Paduan manuscripts of the thirteenth century (Padua, Chapter Library, Epistolary by Giovanni Gaibana, dated 1259; see Miner, 1966, and Rome, 1954, no. 143, pl. XXIX b) and to the "final phase of Sicilian illumination under the Hohenstaufens" (Lattanzi, 1964, pp. 136–144).

Former Collection: Grete Ring, London.
Exhibition: Berkeley, 1963, nos. 14 and 15, pl. XIV.
Literature: Miner, 1966, pp. 471–475.

31 COMB
French or southern Italian?, 12th century
Bone, 12 x 4^1/$_2$ in.
Lent by the Metropolitan Museum of Art (55.193)
The Cloisters Collection, Purchase, 1955

Consisting of a set of fine and large teeth flanking a central panel with an openwork design depicting four stags around a stylized plant, this decorative comb is of the type frequently used for ritual purposes in various Church ceremonies. Normally used in the ritual cleansing of the priest before the celebration of the Mass, it was sometimes used at coronation ceremonies of kings or at the consecration of a bishop (Feasey, 1896). The ceremonial use of the comb must have gone back to the origins of the Christian ritual and may even be derived from pagan practices. A number of elaborate combs of about A.D. 1000 have survived, notably the Comb of St. Loup at Sens, believed to date from the seventh or eighth century (Paris, 1965, no. 813), the Comb of St. Heribert in Cologne of the second half of the ninth century (Cologne, 1964, no. 4), and the comb said to have been used at the coronation of Henry II of the Holy Roman Empire, possibly of the eleventh century, now in Verdun (Cleveland, 1967, II–6).

In comparison with these sumptuous examples, the Cloisters comb is simple, even provincial. Yet it manifests the continuance of an interesting iconography. The heraldic pattern of the four stags derives from Early Christian mosaics and Byzantine reliefs, where such animals are shown either drinking from the fountain of life or standing by the tree of life. This motif derives from a passage in Psalm 41, verse 2: "As the hart longs for flowing streams, so longs my soul for thee, O God." A more literal representation of this theme occurs in one of the mosaics in the Mausoleum of Galla Placidia in Ravenna, on the back of the Pignatta Sarcophagus in the Capella Braccioforte of S. Francesco, Ravenna (Lawrence, 1945, fig. 42), and in a small Coptic tympanum of the seventh century, now in the Louvre (Coche de la Ferté, 1958, no. 9, pp. 19, 89). In the latter two examples, the fountain of life is indicated in a conventionalized manner by an amphora overflowing with water; this is omitted in the Cloisters comb, but it seems probable that the theme is intended to be the same.

The exact origin of the Cloisters comb remains open to question. Somewhat similar flat openwork carving is to be found in a twelfth-century crozier head now in the Louvre (Verrier, 1953, pl. 159) and a thirteenth-century crozier head in the Cathedral Treasury at Vannes (Morbihan) (Paris, 1965, no. 337, pl. 49). Both are thought to be French. But one is also tempted to think of the numerous examples of art displaying a strong Byzantine influence in Italy, the continuing heraldic nature of sculptural decoration as it was applied to the facades of buildings (no. 48), altar rails, and pulpits. In either case, there is a strong likelihood that the design for the comb may have derived from Sassanian-inspired Byzantine textiles, which were imported into both Italy and France in the early Middle Ages and emulated in diverse arts.

32   EUCHARISTIC DOVE*
       French, Limoges, 13th century
       Gilt bronze with champlevé enamel, 7 x 9 in.
       Lent by the Albright-Knox Art Gallery, Buffalo, New York

Since the dove is the symbol of the Holy Ghost, its form becomes an appropriately symbolic container for the Eucharist. The back is hinged so that the Host may be placed inside. The bird was then normally suspended above the altar by chains fastened to the circular base plate, in this case probably attached to the four curving prongs (which, however, may be of somewhat later workmanship).

The smoothly shaped form of the dove is gilt and incised with an overlapping scalelike pattern to suggest feathers. Champlevé enamel roundels and blue, green, and white stripes to emulate the feather patterns decorate the wings and tail. The round plate upon which the dove stands is likewise adorned with champlevé enamel in a circular, quasi-rosette design. A dove on a similar base, considered to date from the second half of the thirteenth century, is in the Metropolitan Museum of Art (no. 17.190.344).

Former Collections: Spitzer Collection; Mortimer L. Schiff, Esq.
Exhibition: Buffalo, 1964, no. 58.
Literature: Spitzer, 1890, I, 118, no. 65, pl. IX; Rupin, 1890, II, 228–230, fig. 295; Vallance, 1893, p. 188; Schiff, 1938, p. 36, no. 94.

33   PYXIS
French, Limoges, 13th century
Gilt copper and champlevé enamel, 4 7/16 x 2 11/16 in.
Lent by the Worcester Art Museum (1949.19)
Austin S. and Sarah C. Garver Fund

The gilt and enameled pyxis was also used to contain the Host (cf. No. 32) and was sometimes used to carry it to the sick for Holy Communion. Cylindrical in form, with a conical lid topped by a ball and cross, the Worcester pyxis is representative of a large number of those boxes that have survived (see Rupin, 1890, pp. 204–209, and Brussels, 1964, nos. 172–180). Yet these pyxes possess such a variety of decoration that no two are the same. The Worcester pyxis is decorated with medallions containing rosettes based on a four-point star, which alternates with curved triangular fields containing loosely entwined foliate forms. Curving *rinceaux* "in reserve" unite the larger patterns in a continuously flowing movement around the sides and the lid.

Former Collection: Brummer Collection.
Exhibition: Tulsa, 1965, no. 113.
Literature: Brummer, 1949, I, 187, no. 710; Worcester Art Museum, *News Bulletin and Calendar*, XV, no. 1 (Oct. 1949), 2; Worcester Art Museum, *Annual Report*, 1950, p. xii; Worcester Art Museum, *News Bulletin and Calendar*, XIX, no. 1 (Oct. 1953), i, fig. 3.

34   RELIQUARY CASKET*
French, Limoges, *c*.1200
Wooden casket with gilt copper and champlevé enamel, 5¹/₂ x
5 7/16 in.
Lent by the Seattle Art Museum (Fr.2.5.1949)
Donald E. Frederick Memorial Collection

Although little is known of the actual sites of production, the manufacture of champlevé enamel objects in the region around Limoges assumed the proportions of a major industry during the twelfth and thirteenth centuries. A large number of resplendent examples of this craft have survived to the present day. The *chasse* from Seattle exemplifies the genre of casket made at the beginning of the thirteenth century to contain venerated relics. The casket itself is made of wood sheathed with copper plaques, which are gilded and decorated with champlevé enamel. In this technique, as opposed to that of cloisonné enamel, depressions are dug into the surface of the metal to hold the molten glass, and considerable use is made of the actual surface of the plaque, the "reserve," which is gilded and incised.

In contrast with the Byzantine plaque from Detroit (No. 16) and earlier Limoges enamels, the figures of the Seattle *chasse* are executed in reserve, incised to render draperies, hands, and feet, and set off against a blue champlevé enamel ground. The figures on the two front plaques, the side, and roof, have separately cast heads in relief, which are applied to the plaque. Stippled, foliate *rinceaux*, terminating in stylized leaves, arch across the ground of champlevé enamel, alternating with medallions containing stylized quatrefoil designs in variegated colors. The front of the casket is adorned with six figures, presumably apostles; the back is decorated with geometric and quasi-foliate patterns. One of the gable ends contains the representation of a single figure, perhaps also an apostle, executed entirely in incised reserve (illustrated in Tulsa, 1965, no. 107). The latter figure, with its swaying pose, its attenuated proportions, and its triple-incised drapery folds manifests a markedly different style of engraving than that displayed on the front panels. In addition, the front and back plaques do not contain the same decorative elements. One is therefore led to conjecture that the plaques were fabricated by different hands, the ends and back being assigned to less skillful artisans, a practice commonly found in numerous other Limoges caskets (Gauthier, 1950, p. 26). On the two front plaques, the rounded edges of the incised lines forming the contours and delineating the drapery folds serve to imply a limited degree of modeled relief, and thereby lend a certain sculptural weightiness to the figures. In this respect, these two panels of the Seattle casket reflect the similar device employed on the Eucharistic coffret in the Limoges Museum attributed to one of the few known Limoges metalworkers, G. Alpais (Gauthier, 1950, pl. 20; Cleveland, 1967, no. III–35, pp. 114–115). This particular technique represents the infusion of nascent Gothic tendencies into the essentially Romanesque style of Limoges in about 1200.

Exhibition: Tulsa, 1965, no. 107.
Literature: Seattle, 1951, p. 115; Thiry, Bennett, and Kamphoefner, 1953, p. 72C (202C and 203C); Moseley, Johnson, and Koenig, 1962, p. 384.

35 PLAQUE FROM A RELIQUARY CASKET: CHRIST IN MAJESTY AND SIGNS OF FOUR EVANGELISTS*
French, Limoges, 2nd quarter of 13th century
Gilt copper with champlevé enamel, appliqué relief figures, $4^3/_4$ x $10^1/_4$ in.
Lent by the Metropolitan Museum of Art (17.190.778)
Gift of J. Pierpont Morgan, 1917

Christ is seated on an enameled rainbow symbolic of the arc of Heaven within an almond-shaped mandorla, or aureole, a schematic device indicating the radiance of divine light about His body. In this case the mandorla is filled with multicolored roundels. He is holding a book in His left hand and making a gesture of benediction with His right. The heads of the four symbols of the Evangelists, derived from the four beasts of the Apocalypse which appeared to St. John in his vision on the Isle of Patmos (Revelations IV, 6–8), appear incised in reserve in medallions in the four corners of the central panel. The two side sections each contain two standing figures, presumably the Evangelists themselves, executed in appliqué relief and set against a dark blue ground divided by two turquoise bands and punctuated with variegated roundels and rosettes.

In contrast with the Seattle casket (No. 32), this plaque from a Limoges *chasse* manifests a further development in the emancipation of the figure from the ground of the enameled panel. In the first decades of the thirteenth century, it became the custom to cast in separate relief, not just the head as in No. 32, but the entire figure in low relief and to attach it to the plaque by rivets (Gauthier, 1950, p. 32). More archaic examples of this form employed appliqué reliefs with draperies and hands simply incised on the curving surface (e.g. a *chasse* with saints in the Musée de Cluny: Gauthier, 1950, pl. 31), whereas in the Metropolitan plaque there is a growing tendency to model the separate volumes of the body through the drapery, as in the knees of Christ and the forearm of the Evangelist on the left.

Former Collections: Hoentschel Collection; J. Pierpont Morgan.
Literature: Pérate, Vol. II, 1911, no. 57, pl. XXXIV.

36   PLAQUE FROM A RELIQUARY CASKET: CRUCIFIXION AND
     MARTYRDOM OF ST. THOMAS BECKET*
     French, Limoges, *c.*1220–1225
     Attributed to Master G. Alpais and his workshop
     Gilt copper with champlevé enamel, $6^5/8$ x $11^3/4$ in.
     Lent by the Cleveland Museum of Art (51.449)
     Purchase from the J. H. Wade Fund

On December 29, 1170, Archbishop Thomas Becket was murdered at a transept altar in Canterbury Cathedral. Becket's subsequent canonization in 1173 raised this heinous crime to the status of martyrdom and provided the inspiration for representation of the event wherever the Saint was venerated (see Borenius, 1932). With the exhumation of his body in 1220 and the distribution of relics over the following twenty years there grew a demand for reliquary caskets to house them. Presumably, the Cleveland plaque is from such a *chasse*. The injection of a new martyrdom into the legends of the Church resulted in the invention of a new iconography, sometimes with a certain amount of license, but within the established conventions for such representation. Although four assailants attacked the Archbishop, a simplified version showing only two is used in the Cleveland plaque, and for that matter in most other depictions of this scene (e.g., Parkhurst, 1952, p. 101, and Borenius, 1932, pp. 84–92, pls. 33–36). Moreover, St. Thomas is shown crowned rather than mitered, which may reflect a misunderstanding of the story by the artisans (Parkhurst, 1952, p. 102, no. 14). The most unusual and perhaps even unique feature of the plaque, as Wixom has pointed out (Cleveland, 1967, p. 116, no. III–36), is the association of the martyrdom scene with that of the Crucifixion. Although a fitting parallel, and one which was apparently encouraged in texts produced at Canterbury at the end of the twelfth century (Cleveland, 1967, p. 116, n. 3), no other examples of this particular iconography are known.

The intent, energetic movement of the striding assailants in the Cleveland plaque set it apart from the usual representations of this scene. When we compare this plaque with the French tradition of moving figures in a dancing pose as exemplified in manuscripts and frescoes in the late eleventh and early twelfth centuries (Cleveland, 1967, p. 116, n. 3) or with the reflection of this style in a Limoges *chasse* in the Louvre Museum (Gauthier, 1950, pl. 29) or even with the mid-twelfth century style of the Master of the Leaping Figures in the Winchester Bible (Winchester Cathedral Library; see Parkhurst, 1952, p. 105), we see the degree to which the artisan of the Cleveland plaque has contrasted the forward rush of the attackers with the stoic, erect pose of the Archbishop as the sword pierces his neck. Stylistic similarities have led Wixom to link the Cleveland plaque with the eucharistic coffret in the Limoges Museum (Cleveland, 1967, p. 116; Gauthier, 1950, pl. 20), which in turn has been associated by Madame Gauthier to a ciborium from Montmajour in the Louvre signed by Master G. Alpais (Cleveland, 1967, p. 114; for the ciborium, see Paris, 1968, no. 385, and Gauthier, 1950, frontis., p. 151). Another reason for associating the Cleveland plaque with the workshop and inspiration of Master G. Alpais may be in the sense of movement alluded to above, for similarly energetic figures may be seen climbing through the entwined *rinceaux* around the base of the Montmajour ciborium.

Former Collections: Tolin; M. G. Chalandon, Lyons; Adolph Loewi, Los Angeles.
Exhibitions: Montreal, 1965, no. 4; Cleveland, 1967, no. III–36.
Literature: Migeon, 1905, p. 28, illus. p. 19, no. 3; Milliken, 1952, pp. 7–8, 13, illus. p. 9; Parkhurst, 1952, p. 101, n. 10, no. 5; p. 102, n. 14; p. 104, n. 15; Wixom, 1967, pp. 116–117, 359.

37   PLAQUE FROM A BOOK COVER: CHRIST IN MAJESTY WITH
     SIGNS OF THE EVANGELISTS*
     French, Limoges, c.1250
     Gilt copper with champlevé enamel, 9¹/₈ x 4³/₄ in.
     Lent by the Allen Memorial Art Museum, Oberlin College

In this enamel plaque from a book cover, the *Majestas Domini* is shown in the same conventional manner as on the plaque from a casket from the

Metropolitan Museum (No. 35), seated on a multicolored arc within a mandorla, surrounded by signs of the four Evangelists. In this case, however, the bodies of Christ and the symbols are executed in incised and gilt reserve, but have appliqué heads. The borders of the plaque, the rainbow, and the mandorla are decorated with wavy champlevé enamel in two shades of blue and white. The ground of the spandrels is light blue, the interior of the mandorla a dark blue, and the roundels and rosettes punctuating the interior of the mandorla contain touches of red, black, green, and yellow enamel. As in the Metropolitan plaque (No. 35), the head of Christ is flanked by the letters Alpha and Omega (No. 8), which in this case are curiously reversed. (This reversal also occurs on similar plaques, one in the Kofler-Truniger Collection in Lucerne—Aachen, 1965, no. E.40 and Cologne, 1968, no. D–37—and on three of the four plaques related to the Oberlin book cover—Stohlman, 1934, figs. 1–3, and Parkhurst, 1952, p. 107.) The Oberlin plaque is practically identical to one of the book-cover plaques in the Metropolitan Museum (Stohlman, 1934, fig. 1).

Former Collections: Otto H. Kahn; Joseph Brummer, New York.
Exhibition: Chapel Hill, 1961, no. 20.
Literature: Parkhurst, 1952, pp. 105–109; Cologne, 1968, no. D–37.

38   ST. JOSEPH*
French, Limoges, 2nd quarter of 13th century
Copper gilt with champlevé enamel, 7 9/16 in.
Lent by the Walters Art Gallery, Baltimore (44.257)

The relief figure of St. Joseph holding an offering of two doves is from a scene, the rest of which is now lost, representing the Presentation of Christ at the Temple.

The figure was attached to the plaque, or ground, by means of two rivets, one at the neck, the other between the legs. In this case, the earlier use of enamel for the draperies of the figures appears on a separately cast figure. (A portion of the enamel has been lost from the lower areas of the drapery revealing the carved, cellular pockets that contained the champlevé enamel.) Enameled relief figures are to be found on a diptych of the Annunciation and Crucifixion in the Musée de Cluny, Paris (Gauthier, 1950, pl. 17), believed to date from the second quarter of the thirteenth century. In the rounded fullness of the face, the tendency to frame the face with a close-fitting cap of hair and stippled beard, the simple, sweeping contours of the form, and the use of drops of blue enamel for the eyes, the figure of St. Joseph is stylistically similar to that of the Musée de Cluny diptych and may have been executed at about the same time.

Former Collection: M. L. (sale, Paris, Dec. 13, 1922, no. 68).

39 VIRGIN AND CHILD
French, Limoges, late 13th century
Copper gilt, 8½ in.
Lent by the Walters Art Gallery, Baltimore (53.3)

The statuette of the Virgin, enthroned and crowned, handing an apple to the Infant Jesus, who sits on her left knee, demonstrates the further evolution of the sculptural properties of Limoges metalwork during the thirteenth century. Now the figure is no longer merely gilt and incised, but rather modeled with greater realization of the volumes of the limbs projecting through the drapery, which itself has weightier and more solid folds. The eyes are now almond-shaped and incised instead of round drops of blue enamel, and the figure was entirely gilt, of which only traces now remain. The hollow statuette was originally attached to a metal or wooden throne, now missing, by means of a metal tab in back and possibly a rivet in front. It was thus a free-standing image of the type frequently employed to contain venerated relics.

The representation of the Virgin holding an apple and giving it to the Christ Child combines a number of symbolic meanings. The apple as the symbol of evil and the source of the fall of man thus imparts to the figure of the Virgin the connotation that she is the New Eve. This then reinforces an additional meaning, for she is offering the apple to Christ, who is considered the New Adam, who, by assuming the burden of all man's sins, assures mankind of ultimate salvation.

The Baltimore figure reflects the style of a number of reliquary statuettes of the enthroned Virgin and Child produced in the region of Limoges and possibly in Spain in the thirteenth century (see Hildburgh, 1955). It is closest to the style of a reliquary in the Metropolitan Museum (no. 25.120. 435: Boston, 1940, No. 237, pl. XXIV) attributed to Limoges in the thirteenth century, while the increased amount of modeling in comparison with the relief figures discussed above (Nos. 33 and 36) and the almost playful gesture of the Christ Child point to a date toward the end of the thirteenth century. A very similar, but somewhat attenuated relief of this type and date is in the Buckingham Collection in Chicago (Chicago, 1945, no. 36).

40 CROZIER HEAD: ST. MICHAEL KILLING THE DRAGON (cover illus.)
French, Limoges, 2nd quarter of 13th century
Gilt copper and champlevé enamel, 12 7/16 in.
Lent by the Detroit Institute of Arts (59.297)
Gift of Mr. and Mrs. Henry Ford II

One of the finest and most resplendent objects of Limoges metalwork in America is this crozier head from the Detroit Institute of Arts. Originally it formed the top portion or crook of a bishop's pastoral staff and was carried by him in religious processions. It is composed of four major parts: a stem, which fitted over the wooden pole of the staff, decorated with a foliate design in reserve against a ground of blue enamel and ribbed by three snakelike reliefs with curling tails; an openwork knob with entwined birds in gilt and stippled copper; a graceful volute, simulating the body of a serpent with glowing blue scales and shimmering gold outlines, which terminates in a snake's head and which is supported by a scroll of foliage; and the striding figure of St. Michael, enclosed by the arching body of the serpent.

The richness of the glittering gold, contrasting with the different shades of blue, and the meticulousness of the stippled patterns and the incised lines delineating the Archangel's feathers and drapery folds make it hard to believe that many crozier heads of this type were perhaps not so highly regarded in their own day and were destined to accompany bishops into their tombs (Robinson, 1962, p. 69). Similar croziers, though not of the quality of the Detroit example, were virtually mass-produced from the last third of the twelfth century through the first half of the thirteenth century, and in his thorough study of them, Marquet de Vasselot (1941) has catalogued more more than two hundred examples. They contain a great variety of representations ranging from stylized foliate forms to animals, to single figures, to scenes with two figures (e.g. No. 39 below). Of the latter type, the most frequently represented was that of St. Michael killing the beast of evil, appropriate to the role of the bishop, whose duty it was to protect his flock from sin and heresy. Almost fifty of them have been catalogued (Marquet de Vasselot, 1941, nos. 122–167), but the design in which the Archangel attacks the volute serpent itself instead of an additional dragon is relatively rare (nos. 160–167). The particular form of the composition, with the upright stance of the Saint, holding a circular shield, paralleled by the downward thrust of the lance into the serpent's neck, while the head arches back to bite the staff, is repeated in only a few croziers (Musée de Cluny in Paris, no. 1581; Marquet de Vasselot, 1941, p. 89, nos. 161–162; and the Metropolitan Museum of Art, no. 163, inv. 10.227). Nothing is known of the early history of this crozier head until it passed through a number of illustrious collections in the nineteenth century. The lack of any dated objects that are stylistically similar makes it difficult to be more precise than the second quarter of the thirteenth century by reason of the perfection of its technical accomplishment. Recently, however, Madame Gauthier has suggested that the Detroit crozier may be placed in the second or third decade of the thirteenth century (Cleveland, 1967, p. 154, n. 2).

Former Collections: Debruge-Duménil, Paris; Soltykoff, Paris; F. M. Gontard and R. Passavant, Frankfurt-am-Main; Madame Walter von Pannwitz, Hartekamp near Haarlem.
Exhibitions: Frankfurt-am-Main, 1914, no. 107; Buffalo, 1964, no. 44; Cleveland, 1967, no. IV–20.

Literature: Labarte, 1847, no. 683; Debruge-Duménil, 1850, no. 683; Didron the Elder, 1859, p. 123 (illus. labeled "Musée du Louvre"); Soltykoff, 1861, no. 195; Darcel, 1861, p. 294; Schilling, 1929, p. 184 illus.; Swarzenski, 1929, no. 113, pl. XXXIX; Marquet de Vasselot, 1936, pp. 138–146; Marquet de Vasselot, 1941, pp. 89, 290, no. 160; Robinson, 1962, pp. 69–71; Detroit, 1966, p. 184 illus.

41 CROZIER HEAD: ANNUNCIATION*
    French, Limoges, 13th century
    Gilt copper and champlevé enamel, 12 5/16 in.
    Lent by the Walters Art Gallery, Baltimore (44.291)

Another frequently represented theme in the crooks of paschal staffs was that of the Annunciation (Marquet de Vasselot, 1941, pp. 76–79, 233–256, nos. 64–102). Belonging to the latest of the three groups of the Annunciation classified by Marquet de Vasselot (p. 78), the Baltimore crozier depicts the Angel Gabriel approaching the already apparently pregnant Mary with a slow dancing step. He holds a lily-topped scepter, a symbol of the Virgin's purity. The volute of the crozier, though diapered in a manner analogous to that of the Detroit crozier (No. 38), terminates in a bud rather than a serpent head, though both devices were used interchangeably. In this case, the shaft below the knob is also diapered instead of foliated.

Former Collection: L. Rosenberg, Paris (sale, Paris, June 12–13, no. 61, illus.).
Literature: Marquet de Vasselot, 1941, p. 244, no. 82.

42 PROCESSIONAL CROSS
    Northeastern Italian, first half of 12th century
    Copper gilt, incised, 20 x 10 in.
    Lent by The Art Museum, Princeton University (97)

Due to the loss of the original attached corpus of Christ, the form of this processional cross appears rather bare. It does reveal, however, the finely textured *opus punctile* and rosette designs that otherwise would have been partly obscured. The end of each arm is decorated with the incised figure of St. Michael above, the mourning Virgin and St. John on each side, and Adam crouching below. Adam as a symbol of fallen mankind appears to be making a gesture of hope upward toward the now missing figure of Christ, whose sacrifice would assure man of salvation. This meaning is further reinforced by the belief that Christ's Cross was erected on Calvary on the site of Adam's grave and that Adam was baptized by Christ's blood. Below the figure of St. Michael, and above the place where Christ's head would have been, is the inscription "IHC NAZAREN REX IVDEORUM."

The reverse of the Princeton cross presents a rich display of incised decoration and a very important inscription. At the juncture of the arms is an almond-shaped mandorla with the Christ in majesty seated on a globe and holding a book, on which are inscribed the Alpha and Omega. He is also holding a long, crossed staff. On the four arms are lively representations of the symbols of the Evangelists, with the winged angel of St. Matthew at the bottom, craning his head back and reaching upward as though to seize the divine inspiration with his hand. Beneath the angel we find that the maker of the cross signed his handiwork with these words, "VOS Q ASPIZITIS DM ROGATE P M TIROLO IAFARINO ME FECIT" (you who look at [this] pray God for me, Tirolus Iafarinus, who made me). The artist has been shown to have come from the region of the Veneto south of the Tirolean Alps, and since the cross is reputed to have come from Belluno, it may well have been produced in that area (Campbell, 1930, p. 97). It is similar to another cross in the Opera del Duomo in Siena dated April 1129 (Campbell, 1930, p. 93), which Toesca has shown to be an imitation of a German cross (1927, I, no. 2, 1144, no. 53) and which Campbell relates to a German cross of the late eleventh century in the Musée de Cluny closely reflecting the superb craftsmanship of Roger of Helmarshausen (1930, p. 94). A cross in Arezzo has been added to this group (Moeller, 1967, p. 88, no. 4), while another one in the Toledo Museum of Art has recently been attributed to Tirolus Iafarinus himself (*Museum News, Toledo Museum of Art*, VIII (1965), 55). The evident link between German metalwork at the end of the eleventh century and similar productions in northern Italy during the first half of the twelfth century, manifested by the Tirolus Iafarinus group of crosses, is reflected in a slightly different group with examples at Duke University and Cologne (Moeller, 1967, no. 34, pp. 86–89).

Exhibitions: Boston, 1940, no. 215; Princeton, 1956, no. 60; Notre Dame, 1960, no. 47.
Literature: Friend, 1925, pp. 132, 140; Campbell, 1930, pp. 90–97; de Francovitch, 1935, p. 8; Moeller, 1967, p. 88.

43   STANDING CROSS*

Mosan or German, Hildesheim or Meuse Valley, 12th–13th century
Gilt bronze, $11^3/4$ x $8^7/8$ in., height with base $17^1/4$ in.
Lent by the Cleveland Museum of Art (44.320)
Purchased from the J. H. Wade Fund

Whereas the Princeton cross (No. 40) was probably intended to be carried on a staff in procession, the Cleveland cross may have been intended to remain on the altar. The plain surfaces of the arms of the cross are bordered by a slightly raised frame, and the inscription "IHC NAZAREN REX IVDEOR[UM]" appears above the head of Christ. The corpus stands erect upon the suppedaneum, the frontal pose broken only by the head inclining forward and to the right. The cross is supported by an elaborate three-legged base of openwork foliate *rinceaux*, which are repeated in the knob above.

The treatment of the corpus, with the smooth surfaces of the body and the sharp lines created by the chest formation and the swelling stomach, tend to separate it from the large number of corpi of Mosan-Rhenish origin (see No. 45 and Cologne, 1964, no. 23), which tend to model the forms more softly and to articulate the ribs, which are not shown here at all. On the other hand, the form of the perizonium, with *V*-shaped folds below a central knot and symmetrically organized folds on either side, reflects the form and treatment found in works usually associated with the circle of Roger of Helmarshausen (see Cologne, 1964, no. 21; Swarzenski, 1955, figs. 237–238). The base of the cross is most closely related to a series of bases and candlesticks believed to have originated in Lorraine and Saxony in the twelfth century, of which some examples are now in Munich and Brussels (Falke and Meyer, 1935, Vol. I, figs. 16, 17, 20). It would seem from these indications that the cross and its corpus are of German workmanship.

Former Collection: Paul Cassirir, Strasbourg.
Exhibition: Buffalo, 1964, no. 36.

44   CORPUS CHRISTI*
     French, Limoges, 13th century
     Gilt copper with champlevé enamel, $9^7/_8$ x $7^3/_4$ in.
     Lent by the Walters Art Gallery, Baltimore (44.250)

The corpus, or body of Christ, in gilt copper and champlevé enamel relief of Limoges workmanship, is from a processional or altar cross of the kind discussed above (Nos. 40 and 41). Presumably the cross itself would have been decorated in champlevé enamel with roundels or a foliate design, imparting a richly contrasting effect of blue and gold.

A distinctive characteristic of the thirteenth-century Limoges corpus is the sweeping curve of the perizonium as it rises over the knees and trails down behind the figure. The legs of the figure are slightly bent, resulting in a gently swaying pose that is indicative of Gothic influences making themselves felt in southern France about the middle of the thirteenth century. The smoothly bulging torso is articulated by an incised ovoid pattern to indicate the rib cage, ribs, and chest, and these lines respond rhythmically to the curving axis of the body. Although the pose hints at developments toward the Gothic, the retention of the four-nail iconography (actually the rivets that attached the relief to the cross), which permits both feet to be placed flat on the suppedaneum, the open-eyed gaze of blue enamel pearls, and the imperial crown with inset cabochons connote the archaic and Romanesque vision of the Christ Triumphant on the Cross rather than the emotional, dead vision which will soon find favor (Nos. 54a and 75). The Baltimore corpus is very close in style and effect to a crucified Christ from the Wasset Collection now in the Musée de Cluny, Paris.

Former Collection: Massarenti Collection, Rome.

45   CORPUS CHRISTI*
     Mosan or German, 12th century
     Gilt bronze, $7^3/_4$ x 7 3/16 in.
     Lent by The Art Museum, Princeton University (56.107)

The fine corpus from Princeton, possibly of Mosan or Rhenish origin, presents a carefully controlled and powerful image of the dead Christ.

Though the figure retains a severe symmetrical frontality, with only a slight bend of the axis in the almost imperceptible inclination of the head to the right, the sagging weight of the torso forces the knees to bend outward while the head also bends forward. Numerous traits reveal a strong German heritage. The general configuration of the perizonium, with slightly converging side panels of folds flanking a central concavity with V-shaped folds, and the rolled fabric at the hips, as well as the central knot, is related to the form observed on the Cleveland corpus (No. 43) and to the circle of Roger of Helmarshausen, and ultimately may derive from the starkly abstracted treatment of the Werden crucifix (see Swarzenski, 1955, fig. 218) of the last quarter of the eleventh century. The Princeton corpus seems to combine the attenuation of the Werden figure with the slouching pose and fine parallel striations indicating the ribs evident in a corpus in Hildesheim attributed to Roger of Helmarshausen (Swarzenski, 1955, fig. 239). At the same time, it must be admitted that there is a gentle softness in the modeling of the forms that relates the corpus to productions from the Meuse Valley, but the conception remains more archaic and rigid than the bending, swaying, more organically modeled forms created in the Meuse under the influence of Renier of Huy in the early twelfth century (see Cologne, 1964, no. 39; Brussels, 1964, nos. 10, 11, 14).

Former Collection: A. M. Friend, Princeton.
Exhibition: Boston, 1940, no. 264.
Literature: Record of the Art Museum, Princeton University, XVI, no. 1 (1957), 13; Green, 1960, pp. 21–25.

46   CORPUS CHRISTI*
     Spanish, early 13th century
     Olivewood, traces of polychrome, $15^5/8 \times 14^1/4$ in.
     Lent by Michael Hall, private collection, New York

The astonishing subtlety of modeling evident in this body of Christ from a crucifix contributes to the gentle but persistent pathos of the representation. Still manifesting the four-nail iconography, the statue retains an erectness and frontality normally found in Romanesque statues of the crucified Christ, but the head inclines to the right, heralding the more emotional Gothic representations. The iconography of this figure is curious, for the left eye is open and the right closed. This extraordinary device heightens the expression of suffering at the moment of death. That we find such an original conception in this statue is entirely consistent with the meticulous articulation of the bodily form, the sensitivity to the representation of the skeleton, evident under the skin, which has been pulled taut by the position of the figure. A less likely, but still possible reason for this might be that the artist was attempting to combine the two natures of Christ on the Cross— the Christ Triumphant and the Dead Christ (see Nos. 11–12, 44–45).

Whether for realism, symbolism, or both, it is an extremely rare if not unique representation.

It is not now possible to date and localize this piece precisely. Yet if a few conjectures might be permitted, it would appear from the still inherent rigidity of the figure, combined with a more sensitive and emotive treatment of the form, that the statue dates from the transitional period from Romanesque into Gothic in Spain, probably in the early thirteenth century. A similar majesty and subtlety can be seen in the ivory corpus at Herfursholm Abbey, believed to be English or Danish from the early thirteenth century (Swarzenski, 1955, fig. 544). But the smoothly clinging perizonium with the overhanging loop of cloth, polychromed with a floral design, reflects in a general way the type found on a number of Spanish Romanesque corpi (e.g., crucifixes at La Seo de Manresa and in the Museum at Vich in Cook, 1950, figs. 295, 297), while the diagonal sweep of the hemline below one knee and above the other reflects a Gothic tendency evident in a crucifix at Torres del Rio (Cook, 1950, fig. 386). Moreover, a crucifix at the Church of San Andres de Cizur Mayor in Navarra evinces a similar breaking away from the hard patterning of the Romanesque toward the softer, more natural, more human articulation of the body found in our piece. Perhaps it evinces, therefore, a native Spanish style in the process of transformation under Gothic influences from the North. Mr. Hall, on the other hand, has suggested that the corpus was carved in the region of Burgos by an itinerant French sculptor. The validity of these suggestions, however, will have to await the test of further research.

47   BRONZE CANDLESTICK*
     German or Mosan, 12th century
     Bronze, height 6⁵/₈ in.
     Lent by the Walters Art Gallery, Baltimore (54.426)

An almost infinite variety of forms, combinations of foliate designs and fantastic, writhing monsters and dragons, may be found as decoration on metal candlesticks produced throughout Europe in the Romanesque period. This single candlestick, one of a pair in Baltimore, is made up of a three-legged, bell-shaped base, the legs taking the form of winged beasts, whose heads serve as feet, a connecting lacelike network of foliage with a naked human figure standing on a lion's head, an openwork knob, and a stem flaring out to the grease pan, supported by three birdlike creatures. The display of exuberant, foliate forms with climbing personages entwined in the curving branches is analogous to that found on sculpted capitals in churches (No. 49) or in illuminated initials of manuscripts (No. 28). The base of the candlestick is quite similar to a number of other candlestick bases in the Wallace Collection, London, the Germanisches Museum, Nürnberg, the church of St. Emmeram, Regensburg, and the church of St. Florian in Austria, and is a type considered by Falke and Meyer to originate from the

Meuse or the Rhine valleys (see Falke and Meyer, 1935, Vol. I, figs. 64–68, nos. 62–67a).

Former Collections: Henri de Lannoy, Paris; Dietz Collection, Coblenz.
Exhibitions: Boston, 1940, no. 269, illus.; Hartford, 1964, no. 16, illus.
Literature: Falke and Meyer, 1935, Vol. I, no. 64, abb. 66.

48 FIVE PLAQUES: SIGNS OF THE EVANGELISTS AND
    ROSETTE*
    Northeastern Italian, Venice?, 12th century
    Marble, from $13^1/4$ x $13^1/4$ x $4^1/4$ to $13^1/2$ x $13^1/2$ x $3^1/2$ in.
    Lent by the Philadelphia Museum of Art ('23–50–1 through 5)

The five relief plaques depicting the four signs of the Evangelists and an elaborately carved rosette within a grape-vine motif are from a six-plaque series that once may have formed an ornamental frieze on the outside of an Italian church. The four signs were presumably flanked by two foliate plaques, of which the rosette is exhibited here; the other is also in the collection of the Philadelphia Museum of Art.

It was the practice throughout Europe, primarily before the development of monumental sculpted portal ensembles, to decorate the façades of churches with applied reliefs exhibiting a great variety of mythical beasts, symbols of the labors of the months, signs of the zodiac, and events from the Bible. Although such reliefs were used as widely as on the façades of Lincoln and Angoulême Cathedrals, their use became a particularly Italian tradition, as exemplified by the façades of S. Michele at Pavia, of S. Pietro at Spoleto, and of S. Zeno at Verona. A similar penchant for scattering relief plaques across a planar façade is to be seen in the tenth-century Church of the Holy Cross at Aghtamar in Armenia, and it is possible that this device was imported into Italy by pilgrims and crusaders during the twelfth century.

Literature: Purves, 1924.

49 DOUBLE CAPITAL: GRIFFINS*
    Spanish, Santa Maria de Aquilar de Campoo, Palencia
    Late 12th or early 13th century
    Stone, $14^5/8$ x $24^5/8$ x $12^3/8$ in.
    Lent by the Fogg Art Museum, Harvard University (1933.99)

The richly carved double capital with two griffins entwined in an acanthus vine comes from the ruins of one of the most important Premonstrian monasteries in Spain, Santa Maria de Aquilar de Campoo in Palencia. The abbey was originally founded in 1161, and the cloister from which the Fogg capital came is believed to have been built in the beginning of the thirteenth century, completed by 1213 and dedicated in 1222 (Lamperez de Romea, 1930, III, 405–410; see Lambert, 1931, pp. 123–125 and pl. XIX for a similar capital *in situ*).

It has been pointed out that two types of capitals coexist in the Campoo cloister (Lambert, 1931, p. 124). The elaborately carved Romanesque type of which the Fogg capital is an example is similar to other twelfth-century Romanesque capitals intended for cloisters. Its paired colonettes are of the sort which one finds from Moissac in Languedoc to Santo Domingo de Silos south of Burgos; in fact it closely resembles those at Silos (see Perez de Urbel, 1930, p. 161). The second type, consisting of very restrained and simplified foliate decoration, resembles capitals at the Cistercian monastery of Las Huelgas, just outside of Burgos. The contrasting styles of the Campoo capitals and the fact of two building campaigns raises the problem of dating the Romanesque type. The original complex was altered to accommodate the building of the new cloister in the early thirteenth century, while the capital appears to be more twelfth century in character. It is possible that there was a portion of an existing cloistered walk dating from the latter half of the twelfth century, and this may have been what was altered and enlarged by the thirteenth-century construction. On the other hand, it is also possible that the later construction was begun by an atelier of stonecarvers who were steeped in the more archaic Romanesque tradition and that they may even have worked alongside other workers who favored the newer and more austere Cistercian style.

Former Collection: Gift of the Republic of Spain through the Museo Arqueologico National and Professor A. Kingsley Porter.
Exhibition: Boston, 1946.
Literature: Bulletin of the Fogg Art Museum, III, no. 2 (1934), 14–17.

50   CAPITAL: VIRGIN AND CHILD AND JOURNEY OF THE
     MAGI*
     French, Rhone Valley, 2nd quarter of 12th century
     Limestone, $8^1/_2$ x $10^1/_2$ x 8 in.
     Lent by the Wadsworth Atheneum, Hartford, Connecticut (1949.181)
     Gift of the Hartford Foundation for Public Giving

The seated Virgin holding the Christ Child on her right knee occupies one side of the capital, while the three Magi on horseback, one pointing to the star of Bethlehem, another holding a falcon, and the third restraining his lively mount proceed around the other three faces on their way to adore the Messiah. A vast quantity of historiated capitals of this type, as distinguished from the inhabited capitals of which No. 49 may be considered an example, were produced in the eleventh and twelfth centuries to adorn the columns and piers of Romanesque churches and cloisters. For the lay public—the inhabitants of local towns and peasants—who attended the services, these historiated capitals frequently related the stories of the Old and New Testaments, while others, depicting assorted virtues and vices, served as visual reminders of the fate of the damned and the rewards of the just. Sometimes a capital would be devoted to a single incident, as in the present example; other times, each individual face carried a different representation. Historiated, inhabited, and foliated capitals normally adorned the columns or engaged shafts of the nave of the church, presenting a rich display of intricate carving, polychromed surfaces, and variety of scenes, such as can still be seen *in situ* at Vezelay, Autun, and Saulieu in Burgundy.

While fulfilling its narrative function in an ingenious manner with the procession encircling the capital, the treatment of the forms in this example —the heavy blocklike masses and squat proportions of the figures—reveals that the carving is of provincial origin. Walter Cahn has effectively demonstrated that the style and manner of composition of the capital has close parallels in the sculpture found in the region around Lyon (Cahn, 1967, p. 49).

Former Collection: Joseph Brummer, New York.
Exhibition: Hartford, 1950, pp. 4, 14.
Literature: Brummer, 1949, II, 208, no. 766; Worcester Art Museum, *Annual Report,* 1950, p. 36; Cahn, 1967, p. 49.

51   CORBEL: MUSICIAN*
French, Provence, 2nd half of 12th century
Limestone, 12 x 7^1/$_2$ in.
Lent by the Wellesley College Art Museum (53.1931.9)

The crouching, crossed-legged figure of a beardless musician playing a viol is carved in relief from a block of stone that may have served as a capital for a pilaster or as a corbel, a projecting support for an architectural element such as a beam. The curve of the musician's neck and shoulders reinforces that of the acanthus leaf arching over the instrument, and this, in conjunction with the two surviving projections of the abacus along the top of the block, emphasizes the original supporting function.

Although executed in a simplified style, the figure reflects characteristics that were prevalent in Provence. The broad, curving surfaces of drapery, only sparsely articulated by ridgelike folds set off by parallel incisions, and the manner of crinkling the folds at the elbow may ultimately derive from such Languedoc sculptures as those on the Port de Miegeville at Saint Sernin at Toulouse or the dismantled portal at Souillac, but resemble more closely the simplified style found in some of the apostle figures at Saint-Gilles-du-Gard (see Porter, 1923, Vol. IX, figs. 1311–1312). Moreover, the detailing of the hair and, notably, the drilling of the pupils of the eyes recall the classicizing tendencies found in the region of Provence (see No. 55). Perhaps the entire conception can be explained as a simplified, provincial reflection of the style found in the reliefs south of the central portal on the façade of St. Gilles. It has been noted that a companion piece, a corbel with a dancer or acrobat, is in the Cloisters Collection in New York (Wellesley, 1964, p. 8).

Former Collection: Joseph Brummer, New York.
Exhibitions: Pennsylvania Museum, 1931; Mt. Holyoke College, 1950.
Literature: Brummer, 1949, I, 141, no. 562, illus.; Wellesley, 1964, p. 8.

52 ELDER OF THE APOCALYPSE*
    Spanish, Castille, early 13th century
    Polychromed wood, 26³/₄ in.
    Lent by the Cincinnati Art Museum (1962.229)

In the apocalyptic vision recounted by St. John in the Book of Revelations there appeared "round the throne [of Christ] . . . twenty-four thrones, and seated on the thrones were twenty-four elders clad in white garments; with golden crowns upon their heads," singing the praises of the Lord. In visual terms, the singing elders were frequently represented playing viols, as in the tympanum at Moissac and in this single wooden figure from Cincinnati.

While retaining some of the squatness and heaviness of the Romanesque style, the statue of the elder of the Apocalypse manifests many of the elements of a nascent Gothic style found in early thirteenth-century Spanish works. Here, the transitional characteristics are reflected in the gently bending posture and in the treatment of the drapery, which no longer clings closely to the figure (No. 51), but begins to assume its own independent volume, weight, and rhythm in the hanging folds.

Literature: Art Quarterly, XXV (1962), 397, illus.

53 COLUMN WITH ADOSSED SAINTS*
    Spanish, Santiago de Compostela, 12th century
    Marble, 45¹/₄ in.
    Lent by the Fogg Art Museum, Harvard University (1933.100)

One of the most interesting and complex art-historical problems is that of the development of the column figure, which suddenly appeared on Abbot Suger's façade of the Abbey of Saint-Denis sometime between 1140 and 1145 and shortly later on the western façade of Chartres Cathedral (after 1145), thereby initiating a series of developments that were to lead to the vast sculptural complexes of the Gothic portals. The column of Spanish origin with three adossed Saints, though perhaps not directly involved with the evolution of the jamb figure, reflects an early stage in the development of this form.

The tall, somewhat flattened figures of St. Simon holding a scroll and Saints Jude and Matthew holding books, all with their names inscribed on their halos, are arranged around a central column. In a careful study of the documents, Porter has shown that this assemblage is one of three surviving figured columns (presumably there were four), which are believed to have been the ones which supported the altar over the tomb of St. James the Major in the church of Santiago de Compostela (1927, pp. 100–103). Appropriately, the complete set would have shown all twelve apostles. Porter has suggested two possible dates for the execution of the columns: they may have been made about 1105, when a new slab was set up on the altar of Santiago de Compostela, in which case they would have been removed to the Benedictine nunnery of San Pelayo de Antealtares in Santiago when the altar was remodeled to receive a silver retable in 1135; or they may have been fabricated at San Pelayo in 1135, when portions of the altar were removed to the convent (p. 110). The former would seem to be a more plausible hypothesis, for there are stylistic similarities between the columns and some of the figures adorning the southern portal of the Cathedral of Santiago, the Puerta de las Platerias. Porter, who first considered the columns "much later" than the portal and dated them in the fourth or fifth decade of the twelfth century (1923, I, 220), came to believe that they were closer in style to those reliefs for the south entrance that were finished by 1103 (1927, p. 110). The figure of St. James donated before 1109, now situated in a frieze above the spandrel over the entrance, marks a development beyond that exemplified by the column figures. However, they most closely resemble the figure of St. Peter to the left of the St. James (see de Palol, 1967, pl. 114, and Gaillard, 1938, pl. CXVII) and the figures set in the arcaded niches of two columns flanking the portal (Palol, 1967, pl. 112). It is therefore possible that the three altar columns reflect an early step, about 1105, in the tendency to detach the relief of the figures from the surface of the block or column.

Former Collection: Benedictine Convent of San Pelayo de Antealtares, Santiago de Compostela; gift of the Republic of Spain through the Museo Arqueologico National and Professor A. Kingsley Porter.
Exhibitions: Boston, 1940, no. 166; The Cloisters, New York, Dec. 1954–Feb. 1955.
Literature: Porter, 1923, I, 220, 222, VI, figs. 705–708; Porter, 1927, pp. 100–103; Porter, 1928, Vol. I, fig. 59; II, 4–7; *Bulletin of the Fogg Art Museum,* III, no. 2 (1934), 14–17.

54   ST. PETER*

South Central France, first half of 12th century
Limestone, 33 x 12 in.
Lent by the Smith College Museum of Art

The monumental relief of St. Peter, shown holding his attribute, a key, and making a gesture of benediction with his right hand, manifests that particular combination of massive, blocklike form and decorative surface pattern that characterizes so much of Romanesque sculpture of the twelfth century. From the nature of the stone and the general aspects of style, the relief has been said to come from a still-undetermined site in the Lot or Corrèze region in south-central France (Payne, 1938). Recently, Moeller has quite rightly connected the Smith relief with four others at Duke University and two at the Rhode Island School of Design (1967, pp. 8–17) and has suggested that there may be yet another two which belong to the series (p. 10). It therefore seems probable that there were originally twelve of these reliefs depicting the twelve apostles, presumably used in some sort of architectural context. Relief plaques with single figures were used in rather loosely organized compositions around portals in the latter part of the eleventh century, as at the Porte de Miègeville at St. Sernin, Toulouse. A now greatly disarranged but analogous grouping also occurred at the Puerta de las Platerias at Santiago (see No. 53). Reliefs with saints or apostles were also employed on square piers in cloister complexes, as at St. Trophime at Arles and St. Pierre at Moissac. However, the particular nature of the reliefs related to the Smith St. Peter suggest another possibility. All the reliefs show the apostles standing on a slanted ledge implying a continuous, unbroken ground line, while three out of the seven published examples show the apostles looking upward at various angles. One is led to conjecture, therefore, that these reliefs may be from a tympanum over a portal. Perhaps they were situated in a monumental lintel under a representation of the *Majestas Domini*, thus accounting for some of the upward-straining poses, analogous to those found in the band of apocalyptic elders in the Moissac tympanum. But it is also possible that some were flanking the mandorla, as in the tympanum at Carennac (see Focillon, 1963, Vol. I, pls. 102, 99). The plausibility of these hypotheses and their attendant details, as well as the problems of more precise localization and dating of all the reliefs, must await the results of further study, which is being conducted at this moment (Moeller, 1967, p. 10).

Former Collection: Joseph Brummer, New York.
Exhibition: Chicago, 1961, no. 39.
Literature: Payne, 1938, pp. 3–6; Moeller, 1967, pp. 8–17.

55   HEAD OF A MAN*
     Southern French, St. Gilles-du-Gard, *c.*1160
     Limestone, 7 25/32 x 5 9/16 in.
     Lent by the Cincinnati Art Museum (1958.548)

Whereas the corbel with the musician (No. 51) is only an approximate reflection of the sculptural style of the region around St. Gilles-du-Gard in Provence, the fine, bearded head from Cincinnati, possibly of a prophet or apostle, is closely related in workmanship and style to the prophets on the façade of St. Gilles (see Porter, 1923, IX, fig. 1313). The waving parallel strands of hair carved in sharp angular ridges, the drilling of the pupils, and the careful articulation of the eyelids and eyebrows indicate that the head is probably by the workshop that executed the prophets south of the central portal on the St. Gilles façade. Opinions concerning the dating of this façade have varied widely—from the end of the eleventh century to the first half of the thirteenth (for a brief summary and further bibliography see Focillon, 1963, I, 128, n. 1)—and even within the more commonly accepted hypothesis of about 1150–1170, one finds a variety of hands working on the twelve apostles. Some evince a strong decorative and planar influence from Languedoc (see Porter, 1923, Vol. IX, fig. 1304), others favor a more volumetric and classicizing approach (fig. 1314). The atelier or hand that is responsible for the group closest to the Cincinnati head appears to fall between these two extremes.

Literature: Art Quarterly, XXII (1959), 275.

56 CROWNED SEATED VIRGIN AND CHILD*
Spanish, Catalan school, 13th century
Gilt and polychromed wood, height 21¹/₂ in.
Lent by the Metropolitan Museum of Art (43.145.1)
Gift of Robert Lehman, 1943

Throughout the Romanesque period the veneration of relics and cult images increased, and pilgrimages to sites of important relics or of miracle-performing statues of the Virgin became almost commonplace. The early representations of the Virgin and Child tended to be rigid in pose, severely frontal in aspect, and strongly didactic in content. Frequently the statues are of the "hodigetria" type—that is, the Virgin is gesturing toward the Child, who is blessing the spectator, to indicate that Christ is the way to salvation.

In the Catalan statue from the Metropolitan Museum, both Mother and Child are in stiff, hieratic, frontal positions. The direction of the Virgin's hand, though holding a fold of drapery, and the gesture of benediction by Christ are both vestiges of the Romanesque idiom. But traces of the newer, Gothic style have already made powerful inroads in what appears at first to be an archaic image. A comparison with truly Romanesque cult images of the Virgin (see Barcelona, 1961, nos. 261, 264, pls. XVII, XIX) reveals that the blocklike solidity of the figures has given way to a more natural, organic articulation of the features. Repetitious patterns and ridges of drapery have become more volumetric and pliant. With the softening of the features and the accompanying humanization of the figures, we have a foretaste of the direction future Gothic art will take (No. 57).

A number of similar statues in this transitional style survive in museums and churches throughout Catalonia and Roussilon (see Cook, 1950, fig. 336). This particular form remained popular in provincial areas of Spain throughout the thirteenth and fourteenth centuries and even later, as evidenced by a group of cult images preserved in the Victoria and Albert Museum in London.

Former Collection: Robert Lehman.

57 HEAD OF A KING*
French, Ile-de-France?, mid or third quarter of 12th century
Limestone, 9⁷/₈ x 8 in.
Lent by Duke University
Brummer Collection

Although severely treated by time, this fragment of a head of a king still manifests the monumental, noble, and compassionate conception of the human figure that became evident in the early stages of the Gothic style. The nose and bottom portion comprising the chin and beard are now missing, yet it is possible to conjecture that it originally displayed an aspect similar to that of the heads of the column figures on Abbot Suger's west portal of Saint-Denis or of the Portail Royale of Chartres. Indeed Moeller has stated that there is evidence that the Duke head is in fact from a column figure and has suggested that it reflects a slightly later phase in the development of Gothic sculpture than the figures of Saint-Denis (see also Ross, 1940, and Stoddard, 1952). Perhaps it is contemporary with the west portals of Chartres, about 1145–1155 (Moeller, 1967, p. 26), for it seems closest to the Old Testament figures to the right of the central portal. Thus we have in the fragmentary piece from Duke the embodiment of a later and highly important tradition whose genesis seems to be reflected in the altar column from Santiago (No. 53).

Former Collection: Ernst Brummer.
Exhibition: Raleigh, 1967, no. 7.
Literature: Moeller, 1967, p. 26, fig. 15.

58   ANGEL*
      French, Autun, Burgundy, end of 13th century?
      Limestone, 15$^1/_2$ in.
      Lent by the Museum of Fine Arts, Boston (42.493)
      Frederick Brown Fund

The full flowering of Gothic art is exemplified in this damaged but appealing relief of an elegantly poised angel. Although the face is mutilated, we may still detect the refined features and sweet, youthful countenance which pervades the arts of the thirteenth and fourteenth centuries and which is exemplified in the famous smiling angel of Reims. The style of the carving is later than that of the Reims figure, manifesting in the contrast of smooth planes of fabric across the torso and the heavy V-shaped folds over the hip a greater similarity with an angel from Poissy (Ile-de-France) now in the Louvre, believed to date from the third quarter of the thirteenth century (Paris, 1950, fig. 114, p. 93). The style of carving also points to developments in Burgundian Gothic sculpture of about the middle of the fourteenth century, as exemplified by the south portal sculptures of the Cathedral of Saint-Etienne at Auxerre (Oursel, 1953, figs. 130–134).

The angel once carried a now indistinguishable object in his left hand and was apparently gesturing toward it with his right. This circumstance leads one to conjecture that he may have been carrying one of the Instruments of the Passion, an object such as the hammer, the nails, the sponge, or the crown of thorns that were used at the Crucifixion. This possibility, together with the relief nature of the carving and the curved right edge of the plaque, suggests that the Boston angel may have been one of a number of such personages holding these objects flanking a central figure of Christ in Majesty in a tympanum, as we find, for instance, in the Last Judgment portal at Bourges. It is also possible, however, that our angel may have been holding a large candle and was flanking a Coronation of the Virgin as at Auxerre (see Oursel, 1953, fig. 126; see also No. 70). Perhaps further study will one day reveal more clearly the original site and context of this charming sculpture.

Former Collection: Abbé Terret, Autun.

59   CROWNED SEATED VIRGIN AND CHILD*
French, Lorraine, *c.*1330–1350
Polychromed sandstone, height 28 in.
Lent by the Philadelphia Museum of Art ('45-25-80)
The George Grey Barnard Collection

With the growing popularity of the cult of the Virgin, which paralleled the development of the Gothic style in France in the latter part of the twelfth and throughout the thirteenth and fourteenth centuries, it became the custom to regard the Virgin Mary both as the Queen of Heaven in all of her courtly splendor and as a humanized symbol of universal maternity. Both of these aspects are combined in the seated Virgin and Child from Philadelphia. She is crowned as in the preceding, more archaic Romanesque example (No. 54), but turns her head slightly toward the Christ Child, whom she helps support. He is half standing on her left knee, intently poring over a book. The sweet visage, gentle look, and tender gestures emphasize the emotional appeal and human aspect of the mother-child relationship. At the same time, the implication of Christ's mission and martyrdom is introduced by the book he is reading, not only a reference to the Gospels, which relate the events of his mature life, but perhaps also to the books of the prophets, whose prophesies he fulfilled.

In comparison with other representations of the Virgin and Child produced during the thirteenth century, the Philadelphia statue seems somewhat squat in proportion, with the knees and legs enveloped in a voluminous mass of drapery. This particular style seems to have been prevalent in the region of Lorraine; the most famous example is a Virgin at St. Dié, and a number of other similar statues have survived in that region. Most similar to the Philadelphia Virgin is a marble, seated Virgin and Child in Aachen Cathedral (Beenken, 1927, pp. 93 ff. and fig. 51; see also fig. 49), considered to date from the 1320's, and a statue in the Cloisters Collection (no. 25.120.250: Forsyth, 1936, fig. 33). Passages in the treatment of the drapery of the Cloisters statue are almost identical to elements in the Philadelphia Virgin. It is interesting to note that both pieces were in the collection of George Grey Barnard, and the Cloisters example was acquired by him along with several others from a ruined church in Toul (Meurthe-et-Moselle) in Lorraine. Although not mentioned by Forsyth (1936) in his study of the St. Dié–type Virgin, it is possible that the Philadelphia statue also comes from the region of Toul, if not from the same workshop as the Cloisters example.

Former Collection: George Grey Barnard.
Literature: Weinberger, 1941, p. 17, no. 80, pl. XXIII.

60 YOUTHFUL HEAD*
French, Reims?, 2nd quarter of 13th century
Limestone with traces of polychrome, 8 x 6¼ in.
Lent by Duke University
Brummer Collection

Embodying all the freshness and serenity of a revived interest in representing, even idealizing, the human figure, the softened and generalized features
of this youthful head recall, at first glance, the almost classical composure
of the Virgin of the Visitation group on the west façade of Reims Cathedral.
Indeed, Moeller has suggested that this head, which apparently has been
broken from a relief, is similar in scale and style to those found in the
tympanum and lintel of the St. Sixtus portal on the north transept of Reims
Cathedral (1967, p. 36; Moeller refers to similar heads in the Louvre but
does not cite the reference, and a search of the Louvre Catalogue, Paris,
1950, has not revealed them). The sculptures of this portal, it is now generally agreed, date from 1224 or 1225 to no later than 1231 and therefore
precede and lead to the ultimate development of the classicizing figures of
the west façade of about 1240. A comparison of the north portal sculptures
with the Duke example, however, reveals the latter to be a slightly more
organically developed conception than the first group of tympanum figures
(see Frisch, 1960, figs. 17–18), while the linear rather than spottily drilled
hair-style differentiates it from the prevailing effect of such figures as
Angel VII (figs. 13 and 33). It would appear to be closest to the north
transept figure of Eve, which has been said to have been strongly influenced
by a sculptor from Amiens (fig. 38, p. 23), and both examples appear to
represent the stage of development just before the creation of the Virgin
of the Visitation on the west portal.

Former Collection: Ernst Brummer.
Exhibition: Raleigh, 1967, no. 11.
Literature: Moeller, 1967, no. 11, p. 36, fig. 22.

61 CANDLEHOLDER OR ALTAR SUPPORT: KNEELING PAGE*
Southern Italian, mid 13th century
Marble, 16½ in.
Lent by Michael Hall, private collection, New York

The kneeling figure of a page may once have been an altar support or a
candleholder as suggested by the platform and iron spike supported on its
left shoulder. The implied weight of the burden is emphasized by the
swath of folded material from the page's costume thrown over the shoulder
to cushion the platform. In pose and in the details of costume, a high-
necked, closely fitting tunic, a broadly pleated skirt, and a circular linen cap
held on by a chin strap, the kneeling page is almost identical with a slightly
larger statue in the Rockhill Nelson Gallery of Art in Kansas City (height,
24¼ in.: Valentiner, 1955, and Kansas City, 1959, p. 50). Valentiner dem-

onstrated that the Kansas City piece is related to similar sculptures produced in southern Italy under the patronage of the Hohenstaufen emperor Frederick II (d. 1250) and of his son Manfred (d. 1266), particularly to two candlesticks that may have flanked a statue of a kneeling knight, tentatively identified by Valentiner as Manfred himself (Valentiner, 1955, figs. 1, 4, 5, and pp. 16–19). Both the Kansas City page and the present statue reflect the compact, simple volumes and the technique of drilling the eyes and filling them with lead pupils (still present in the Kansas City piece; missing here) that reflect the continuing Romanesque tendencies in Italian sculpture of the thirteenth century. In both, the costumes emulate the latest fashions of the Gothic North, which also permeated the illustrations of Frederick II's famous treatise on falconry, *De arte venandi cum Avibus* (Rome, Biblioteca Vaticana, MS. Vat. Palat. Lat. 1071; cf. Valentiner, 1955, fig. 2).

The present example, however, could not have been the companion piece to the one mentioned above, for it faces the same way rather than forming a counterpart, and it is smaller and somewhat less carefully worked out in detail (e.g., the belt present in the Kansas City statue is not present here). A number of similar statuettes that came on to the art market shortly after World War II are believed to be modern imitations of the Kansas piece (Valentiner, 1955, p. 26, n. 1); however, Frederico Zeri has indicated by personal communication with the owner that this statue is said to have been found in a ruined church at Pontremoli, north of Lucca.

Former Collection: Dr. W. R. Valentiner.
Exhibition: San Francisco, 1964, no. 66.

62 FRAGMENT OF A SARCOPHAGUS: DANIEL BETWEEN TWO LIONS*
Northeastern Italian, Venice?, c.1340–1360
Marble, 25$^1/_2$ in.
Lent by Michael Hall Fine Arts, Inc., New York

In Italy the advent of the Gothic style manifested itself in a different manner than it did north of the Alps. Strong classical strains had lent a particular robustness to Italian Romanesque sculpture, while the influence of the hieratic and decorative aspects of Byzantine art infused Italian works with an overwhelming monumentality and never-ending richness. It is the fusion of all these elements with a nascent Gothic style that underlies the particular combination of dignity and courtliness in the kneeling page (No. 61). In the relief of the prophet Daniel flanked by two lions, however, these same elements seem to be combined with a certain flavor of Tuscan protohumanism to yield a monumental, forthright, and self-assured portrayal.

The relief of Daniel is probably from the corner of a sarcophagus, to judge from the column along the right side and the diagonal slots for iron clamps in the top and bottom edges, which would have held the end in place. This relief is representative of a great number of sarcophagi, or fragments thereof, which were produced in the region of Venice throughout the fourteenth century. Examples now preserved in the Estense Collection in Vienna (Planiscig, 1919) reveal that these sarcophagi usually consisted of figurative reliefs flanking a simple inscribed or emblazoned central panel. If more figures adorned the front of the sarcophagus, they were placed against a ground enframed by incised lines. It appears that the Daniel occupied the standard position between the corner column and such an enframed ground, as indicated by the incised lines and the vestige of an upper corner to his right.

The figure of Daniel seems closest to a fragment containing an annunciate angel (Planiscig, 1919, p. 20, no. 28) of approximately the same height, in which the treatment of hair, drapery, and the spiral column with foliate capital are all very similar. Planiscig dates the Estense figure to about 1320–1330, and a comparison with the Daniel reveals that it is somewhat more blocky, solid, and rigid in pose. Because the Daniel turns slightly on his axis and evinces a greater relaxation of pose and demeanor, the relief would seem to be slightly later, perhaps from about 1340–1360.

Former Collection: Joseph Brummer, New York.

63   FOLIO FROM ANTIPHONAL: INITIAL WITH ANNUNCIA-
      TION TO ZACHARIAS*
      Flemish, Abbey of Cambron, late 13th century
      Tempera and gold leaf on vellum, 18^1/$_2$ x 11^1/$_2$ in.
      Lent by the Lansburgh–Colorado College Collection, Colorado Springs

The handsome illuminated page from a Mass book, containing the antiphons or musical responses sung by the choir during the performance of the Mass, reveals not only the fine Gothic script but also the form of late thirteenth-century musical notation. The elaborate historiated initial introduced the verses to be sung at the feast of St. John the Baptist. The illustration shows Zacharias, the father of St. John, holding a censer at the high altar. He is interrupted by a descending angel, who carries a scroll with the words "Ne timeus Zacharii." Presumably this is the annunciation to Zacharias, when the angel informed him that his wife, Elizabeth, would give birth to the Baptist.

The decoration of the page reveals the new forms adopted by Gothic illuminators in the second half of the thirteenth century. Whereas Romanesque initials tended to be contained by backgrounds (see the tail of the Q in No. 26), Gothic initials break out of the frame, the staff of the letter growing freely down the left margin in a thick, pigmented bar with heavy angular or cusped joints at the corners and terminals. Beasts intertwined in fleshy tendrils (No. 27) give way to a profusion of stylized foliage.

The style of the figures also mirrors the developments of the period. After the first monumental phase of the Gothic period, forms tended to become less substantial, less differentiated, and even more carelessly drawn. In manuscript illumination this style takes the form of a more sketchy, linear rendition of the figures, less modeling of the features and draperies, and the constant repetition of the same facial types. Yet in the superb Zacharias initial, we can see that in the hands of a competent craftsman the style yields an extraordinary finesse and delicacy of touch. The hair-thin lines astound the beholder with the artist's deftness and control of the brush. Other pages from this manuscript are said to be in the National-museum, Stockholm.

Former Collection: Dr. Eric Miller.

64   FOLIO FROM A PSALTER: INITIAL WITH THE ANOINTING OF DAVID?†
French, *c.*1280
Burnished gold leaf and tempera on vellum, 10 3/16 x 7 9/16 in.
Lent by the Lansburgh–Colorado College Collection, Colorado Springs

Highly burnished gold leaf provides a glittering backdrop for the pink, brown, and blue pigmented figures within the historiated initial *D* of this magnificent illuminated folio from a psalter. Introducing the first line of Psalm 26, the initial contains a scene that may be of Saul anointing David while a high priest looks on, though Saul's halo does not seem justifiable and may represent an error on the part of the illuminator. Reflections of earlier techniques of manuscript decoration are evident in the placing of the initial and *incipit* of the psalm within a framed panel and in setting off the dragons and foliate *rinceaux* in the left and bottom margins against an irregularly shaped bar with burnished gold background. Nevertheless, the tendency to provide a decorative foliate frame for the text, which gains momentum in the Gothic period, has already become firmly established.

The style of the figures reflects a seldom-achieved high point of precision and monumentality just before or contemporary with the Parisian illumina-tor Maître Honoré. Yet the suggestion of volume through the use of line rather than shading points to a date just prior to the overwhelming influence of his style on French illumination after 1290. The sumptuous quality of the decoration, the use of gold lettering against the blue and gold bands, the unusual depiction of stylized birds in filigree in the smaller initials, the glowing, diapered background to the initial, reminiscent of the forms and effects evident in stained-glass windows, and the elegantly poised figures all confirm that this is a folio from a manuscript of the highest quality.

Literature: Colorado College Magazine, II, no. 3 (Summer, 1967), 12, illus.

65 FOLIO FROM A GRADUAL: INITIAL WITH RESURRECTION*
German, Upper Rhine Valley, c.1300
Gold and tempera on vellum, 16 x 12³/₄ in.
Lent by The Art Museum, Princeton University (29.154a)

Probably illuminated in the region of the Rhine Valley about 1300, this folio from a Gradual, or Mass Book with all the sung responses for the choir, reflects no one style of decoration, but rather a merging of influences from areas in both France and Germany. The large initial R contains a representation of the Resurrection of Christ set against a burnished gold ground. In the intensity of the gaze of Christ and the crinkles and slightly softened folds of drapery the miniature reflects the style of illumination exemplified by the Heisterbach Bible (Berlin, Staatliche Bibliothek, Cod. Theol. lat. fol. 379: Swarzenski, 1936, I, 91–95, no. 10, II, figs. 61–156), produced in Cologne about 1240, and the Aschaffenburg Gospels (Aschaffenburg, Hofbibliothek, Cod. 13: Boeckler, 1953, pl. 72), produced in Mainz about 1260. But the more flowing drapery style, together with the greater angularity of the Gothic script and the developed foliate sprays sprouting from the initial, points to a somewhat later date. By and large, German illuminators did not adopt the French penchant for developing marginal decoration in the manner we have seen above (Nos. 63 and 64), but tended to retain the extensions of the initials within framed panels related to the Romanesque system (No. 26). Thus the presence of the cusped and foliated *rinceaux*, spreading freely within the margins, appears to be unusual in this otherwise Germanic example. Stylized maple-leaf foliage does occur, however, within the confines of initial decoration in some manuscripts of the Mainz school (see Hamburg, Stadtliche Bibliothek, Cod. In. Scrinio 1: Swarzenski, 1936, Vol. II, fig. 261) of approximately 1260. Thus we may conjecture that the manuscript from which this folio came may have been illuminated in the region of the Rhine Valley between Cologne and Mainz in an atelier influenced by the Franco-Flemish mode of border decoration.

Former Collections: Gélis-Didot (sale, Paris, April 12, 1897); Leclerq, gift of Junius S. Morgan, 1929.
Exhibition: Boston, 1940, no. 45.
Literature: Ricci, 1937, II, 1175, no. 10.

66 BOOK OF HOURS
Northern French or Flemish, c.1300
Tempera and gold on vellum, 108 folios, 4 x 2³/₄ in.
Text in Latin, 10 lines
Lent by the Walters Art Gallery, Baltimore (MS. W.87)

Written in French and probably originating in the area that is now northern France or southern Belgium, this diminutive Book of Hours contains amusing drolleries in the margins of all its pages. A heavy staff emanating from the decorated initials in the text has now grown into both the left and bottom margins. Grotesque heads and thin arching sprays with stylized ivy leaves sprout from cusped joints. Although the style of the marginalia is crude, there is an endless variety of representations, some moralistic, some satirical, and some humorous. From this point on, the evolution of the Book of Hours and its decoration, created expressly for the private devotions of the laity rather than for the liturgical use of the clergy, becomes one of the most significant in the development of manuscript illumination (see No. 103).

Former Collection: Gruel and Engelman, no. 1019.
Literature: de Ricci, 1935, I, 783, no. 162; Randall, 1966, p. 38, figs. 107, 436.

67   STAINED GLASS ROUNDEL: HEAD OF AN ANGEL
     English, late 14th century
     Stained and leaded glass, diameter 16¹/₂ in.
     Lent by The Art Museum, Princeton University (46.98)

A number of problems concerning this roundel of stained glass depicting the head of an angel must remain unresolved for the moment. It is considered to be an example of late fourteenth-century English stained glass (*Record of the Art Museum, Princeton University,* VI, nos. 1–2 [1947], 8), but it manifests both earlier and later characteristics. The deeply colored draperies and background are perhaps indicative of an earlier date, but the strong grisaille modeling of the face, the heavy-lidded eyes, the pouting mouth, and the strongly accentuated nose reflect developments that we find in manuscript illumination in the last quarter of the thirteenth century. These physiognomic traits may be observed in the frontispiece to the *Liber Regalis* in the Library of Westminster Abbey, which dates from about 1382 (Rickert, 1965, pl. 159), in the subtly executed angels of the Wilton diptych, which may date from 1380–1395 (Rickert, 1965, fig. 161), and in a harder and more exaggerated manner in a pair of roundels in the Metropolitan Museum considered to date from the last half of the fifteenth century (Binghamton, 1968, nos. 24–25). The first two may have been executed in London; the latter has been linked with York. The origin of the present window must still remain open to question.

It should be noted that the roundel may have been the donation of a man and wife; the border is decorated with two initials, an *M* and a *G*, each occurring twice and each entwined in a knotted cord of the kind frequently used in marriage monograms.

Former Collection: Bashford Dean, New York.
Literature: Record of the Art Museum, Princeton University, VI, nos. 1–2 (1947), 8.

68 FRAGMENT OF STAINED GLASS: QUATREFOIL AND ROSETTE
German, Upper Rhine Valley, 14th century
Stained glass, 12 3/16 x 11⅝ in.
Lent by The Art Museum, Princeton University (46.97)

This purely decorative plaque of stained glass consists of a quatrefoil design surrounding two concentric circles with a rosette in the center. The surface is enlivened by foliate decoration set off against crosshatching, all of which is painted on the segments of glass with black paint. Purely decorative panels of this kind, making use of painted ornament on white or stained yellow glass with only a few contrasting colors, became prevalent in the later Gothic period. This panel is believed to have been manufactured in the Upper Rhine Valley in the fourteenth century.

Former Collections: Didson, Paris; Bashford Dean, New York.
Literature: Record of the Art Museum, Princeton University, VI, nos. 1–2 (1947), 8.

69 AQUAMANILE IN THE FORM OF A LION*
Flemish or German, 14th century
Bronze, 9 1/16 in.
Lent by the Walters Art Gallery, Baltimore (53.25)

As the name implies, an aquamanile is a vessel used to contain water for the washing of the hands of the priest before celebrating the Mass. These ewers were made in a great variety of forms—knights on horseback, dragons, birds, and griffins—but one of the most frequently employed forms was that of a lion. The body was hollow, and in the Baltimore example an opening between the ears was used for filling, while the spout in the mouth was used for pouring. Usually a handle was provided either by curving the tail of the animal up over its back and joining it at the neck or by placing a dragon or some other figure in this position; in the Baltimore example this is missing. The head is turned to the left, and the face is rendered in what seems to be a smiling, feline expression. The finely wrought features, the carefully incised ruff of stylized curling locks forming the mane, the arched engraved lines under the belly, the rhythmic arabesques of lines dividing the legs from the body, and the pleasing curves of the haunches and legs imbue this object with a sprightly and vivacious spirit. A curious inscription in Hebrew on the left flank of the beast suggests that this aquamanile was once in a synagogue.

Former Collection: Stein, Paris (sale, Paris, 1899, p. 30, no. 139, illus.).

70 IVORY CROZIER HEAD: VIRGIN AND CHILD BETWEEN TWO ANGELS;* CRUCIFIXION
French, Paris, 14th century
Ivory, 9½ x 4⅛ in.
Lent by the Walters Art Gallery, Baltimore (71.132)

On one side of the crozier head the crowned Virgin stands supporting the Christ Child on her left hip. She offers him a flower while two candle-bearing angels look on. On the reverse side, Christ appears on the Cross between the mourning figures of the Virgin and St. John. These two juxtaposed scenes appear above the serpent, the symbol of evil, which is coiled between the cross and the knob of the crozier. The staff, knob, and crook are covered with stylized maple leaves; three of them project outward from the curvature as though to give it corners, but one of these "ears" and the base appear to be modern additions. Traces of polychrome are evident on some of the figures, attesting to the richness of effect of such objects in their original condition. The workmanship of this crozier is rather crude, evidence of the vast production of carved ivories in numerous ateliers in Paris and perhaps throughout Europe in the fourteenth century.

An almost identical crozier head, which was also in the Spitzer Collection in the nineteenth century, and one with which the Baltimore crozier frequently has been confused, is in the Wernher Collection at Luton Hoo, England.

Former Collections: Campe Collection, Hamburg; Spitzer Collection, Paris.
Literature: Spitzer, 1890, Vol. I, no. 92 (illus. erroneously listed as no. 92; it depicts no. 91); Koechlin, 1924, II, 272, no. 761. (No. 761 appears to be the crozier now in Baltimore; Koechlin erroneously cites it as no. 91 in the Spitzer Catalogue with illustration. As noted above, the illustration is wrongly labeled; it depicts no. 91 and corresponds in all details with the crozier at Luton Hoo cited above. The Baltimore crozier is, therefore, probably no. 92. This error is perpetrated in other literature cited by Koechlin, which actually refer to no. 91 and not to the Baltimore crozier.)

71   FOLDING SHRINE: VIRGIN AND CHILD*
     French, first half of 14th century
     Atelier of the Tabernacles of the Virgin
     Ivory, $8^{1}/_{2}$ x $9^{1}/_{4}$ in.
     Lent by the Metropolitan Museum of Art (17.190.201)
     Gift of J. Pierpont Morgan, 1917

Throughout the fourteenth century the increased demand for objects to adorn small chapels and family altars for private devotions resulted in a vast production of small, portable folding tabernacles of metalwork, ivory, or painted panels. Among the most prolific producers of these votive objects were the ivory carvers, who are thought to have been centered mostly in Paris, but who were no doubt active throughout the rest of Europe as well.

Attributed by Koechlin to a Parisian workshop he called the Atelier of the Tabernacles of the Virgin (Koechlin, 1905), the present folding shrine contains a statuette of the Virgin and Child and carved reliefs on the wings, depicting incidents concerning the birth of Christ. The statuette is situated under a projecting porch, of which the columns are now missing. The swaying pose, the voluminous drapery, accentuating the curve of her body and lending visual support to the Christ Child seated in the crook of her left arm, and above all the aristocratic demeanor, idealization of the features, and tender gaze as she inclines her head toward the infant, all reflect the courtly elegance and love of refinement that dominated the Gothic art of the fourteenth century. The wings, each made in two parts so as to completely enclose the porch and statuette when closed, are executed in a rough, caricatural style. On the upper left are the *Annunciation* and the *Visitation*, and below, occupying two compartments, are the three Magi, two standing and one kneeling and holding his crown. The *Nativity*, consisting of Joseph seated and the Virgin reclining, and a donkey and a cow contemplating the swaddled baby in the manger above, occupies the two upper sections of the right wings, while below occurs the *Presentation at the Temple,* also in two compartments.

The placement of these figures within architectural frames, the general treatment of drapery and physiognomy, and even the composition of the scenes are closely related to the art of manuscript illuminators of the late thirteenth and entire fourteenth centuries. Identical compositions occur again and again, not only copied from ivory to ivory, but also among the manuscripts of the period, as certain designs became models for mass production by the two crafts, which had become virtual industries. For this reason the classification of Gothic ivories given by Koechlin (1924, Vols. I–III) cannot be considered an accurate reflection of date, locale, or even atelier. If one compares the Metropolitan tabernacle with those around which Koechlin builds his group of the Atelier of the Tabernacles of the Virgin (a tabernacle in Berlin, Vol. II, no. 134 *bis,* and one in the British Museum, Vol. II, no. 134), one finds that the general format, organization of the wings, and placement of the statuette are similar, but that there are distinctive variations in the style of carving that may go beyond differences between artisans in a single atelier.

Former Collection: Charles Mège.
Exhibition: Paris, 1889, no. 118.
Literature: Koechlin, 1905, pp. 460–461; Migeon, 1909, p. 6, no. 86; Koechlin, 1924, I, 128, II, no. 136.

72   STATUETTE OF VIRGIN AND CHILD*
     French, beginning of 14th century
     Ivory, $7^7/_8$ in.
     Lent by the Walters Art Gallery, Baltimore (71.128)

The standing, crowned Virgin, swaying slightly to the left to support the infant Jesus on her hip, is the embodiment of the Gothic vision of the aristocratic yet tender and maternal Queen of Heaven. Emulating the form, pose, and sweetness of countenance of larger statues of the Virgin such as the Vièrge d'Oré of Amiens and the Virgin of Notre Dame, Paris, ivory statuettes of this sort were manufactured by the hundreds for private chapels and altars. Commensurate with the devotional purpose and small scale of these images is their pervading sense of intimacy. In the Baltimore statuette, the Virgin is holding the symbolic apple, but the didactic emphasis is dissipated, since the Child plays with the end of her veil. The refinement of the features, the squinting eyes, and the complicated elaboration of the drapery folds relate the Baltimore statuette in a general way to a group of ivories produced about 1300, of which the most exquisite example is the famous Vièrge de la Sainte Chapelle in the Louvre (Cleveland, 1967, no. V–7).

73   RELIEF OF SEATED VIRGIN AND CHILD
French, 14th century
Ivory, 6 5/16 in.
Lent by the Walters Art Gallery, Baltimore (71.90)

Carved in low relief, this representation of the seated Virgin and Child shows the Christ Child standing on the Virgin's knee and playing with her veil with his right hand. The madonna originally wore a crown, of which only portions of the headband remain. Although the conventions of physiognomy and drapery used in this relief are essentially those found in the statuette of the standing Virgin (No. 72) and may be derived from that group, there is a fleshiness about the face and a weightiness about the torso indicative of a later and perhaps provincial atelier.

74   DIPTYCH: SCENES OF LIFE OF CHRIST AND LIFE OF THE VIRGIN*
French, first half of 14th century
Ivory, 9 13/16 x 10³/₈ in.
Lent by the Detroit Institute of Arts (40.165)
Gift of Robert H. Tannahill

Small portable diptychs and triptychs were frequently employed instead of folding tabernacles as miniature altarpieces for private devotions. In the case of the Detroit diptych, a continuous narrative from the lower left corner with the *Annunciation* to the upper right with the *Coronation of the Virgin* presents the interwoven stories of the life of the Virgin and of the life of Christ for the viewer's contemplation. The scenes are as follows: the *Annunciation*, the *Visitation*, the *Annunciation to the Shepherds*, the *Nativity*, the *Adoration of the Magi*, the *Presentation at the Temple*, *Christ Found among the Doctors*, the *Miracle at the Marriage of Cana*, the *Last Supper*, the *Crucifixion*, the *Resurrection*, the *Ascension*, the *Pentecost*, and the *Coronation of the Virgin*.

Each of the panels of the diptych is divided into three registers by two horizontal ledges decorated with five-petaled roses. Maskell (1872) thought all ivories with this device were English; Koechlin (1918) attributed them to a Parisian atelier "à decor de Roses"; and subsequently it has been demonstrated that this motif was used in both France and Italy (Egbert, 1929, and Morey, 1936). With respect to the Detroit diptych, Robinson (1941) has presented strong evidence in support of its origin in France, based on the observation that the type of hinge employed to attach the two plaques is common to the North. He observed that the Detroit diptych was iconographically and compositionally similar to a diptych formerly in the Mège Collection (Migeon, 1909, p. 8; now in the Louvre, Mège bequest, 1958). Although the Mège diptych contained exactly the same number and disposition of scenes as the Detroit example, Robinson quite rightly noted the entirely different style, which in addition to being "more intense, . . . restive and emotional" is more deeply and sharply carved. Moreover, many of the postures and attitudes in the Mège diptych differ considerably from the Detroit figures. Another diptych, in the Archeological Museum in Lille (Koechlin, 1918, pp. 232–233, illus., and 1924, Vol. II, no. 250), presents scenes that are closer compositionally, but that are arranged differently in their placement on the plaques. Here again, the carving is deeper, and the figures more crowded. In comparison, the Detroit diptych tells its story in a calmer, clearer, more measured cadence.

Former Collections: Said to have come from the Cathedral Treasury, Laon; Sulzbach Collection.
Exhibition: Detroit, 1928, no. 56.
Literature: Heil, 1929, p. 74 and illus., p. 79; Robinson, 1941, pp. 74–77; *Art Quarterly,* IV (1941), 151–152, illus., p. 146; Detroit, 1966, p. 185.

75   DIPTYCH: SCENES FROM THE LIFE OF CHRIST*
      French, mid or second half of 14th century
      Ivory, 4⁷/₈ x 4 13/16 in.
      Lent by Detroit Institute of Arts (43.455)
      Gift of Robert H. Tannahill

Four scenes from the Life of Christ—the *Nativity,* the *Adoration of the Magi,* the *Presentation at the Temple,* and the *Crucifixion*—are set within quatrefoil medallions on this small ivory diptych. The juxtaposition of these scenes and the use of the quatrefoil frame reflect the similar device employed by manuscript illuminators in their productions of the latter half of the fourteenth century (e.g., the *Esthetics* of Aristotle, Brussels, Bibliothèque Royale, MS. 9505–6, f. 2v., of about 1376 in Delaissé, 1965, p. 79). The frequency with which identical devices and even scenes are repeated in ivories and in miniatures of manuscripts reveals that both trades were employing similar models. It is not uncommon, therefore, to find parallels not only in the groupings of the figures, but also in the gestures and expressions.

Former Collection: Prof. A. Gilbert, Paris (sale, Hotel Druot, Paris, Nov. 29–30, Dec. 1, 1927, no. 27).
Exhibition: Detroit, 1928, no. 59.
Literature: Robinson, 1944, p. 40, illus., p. 41.

76   DIPTYCH: VIRGIN AND CHILD AND CRUCIFIXION*
      French, 2nd quarter of 14th century
      Ivory 5 7/16 x 6⁵/₈ in.
      Lent by the Walters Art Gallery, Baltimore (71.178)

One of the most frequently encountered forms of the ivory diptych is that in which the Virgin and Child are represented on one leaf and the Crucifixion on the other. In the presentation of these two scenes, one reflecting the worship of the Virgin, the other the sacrifice of Christ on the Cross, we have essentially the same juxtaposition that was also used on numerous ivory crozier heads (see no. 70). In the Baltimore diptych, it is actually the *Coronation of the Virgin* that is shown: an angel descends from Heaven and places the crown on her head as she offers a bunch of flowers to the Christ Child, whom she holds in the crook of her arm; two candle-bearing angels look on.

The *Crucifixion* is a more elaborate version than that encountered on the crozier mentioned above. To the mourning figures of the Virgin and St. John have been added the two other Marys, who support the swooning Virgin, and also two mocking figures behind St. John. This expanded treatment of the Crucifixion theme ultimately derives from the influence of paintings by Duccio in the early fourteenth century, as they were transposed and injected into French manuscript illumination by Jean Pucelle in the 1320's (see Morand, 1962, pl. 10, c and d). Indeed, the deeper carving of this diptych, the accentuated, swaying poses of the figures, the sharply broken S-curve of the body of Christ on the Cross, and the fine, multifarious folds of drapery swirling around the forms closely reflect the new direction given to manuscript illumination by Pucelle. But it should be noted that the influences may have gone both ways. One of the far-reaching contributions of Pucelle to the art of the miniature was the introduction of *grisaille*, or modeling of the forms in subtle shades of black and grey to white, and this in turn may well have been derived from a sensitivity to the effects achieved by the interplay of light across the finely carved forms of ivory reliefs.

Architectural frames surmount the scenes on both panels. Consisting of trilobed arches within a gable adorned with crochets and a fleuron at the top and supported by corbels just above the heads of the figures, these forms reflect the increasing elaboration of similar elements in the Gothic buildings of the period. To fill in the spandrels or spaces above the gables, the artist has placed a quatrefoil within a circle, punctuated by a projecting circular hub in each. Visually, these devices combine to lend a highly activated and lace-like quality to the frame, which is consistent with the swaying postures, swirling draperies, and intensified emotional impact of the scenes below.

77   DIPTYCH: NATIVITY AND CRUCIFIXION*
     French, mid 14th century
     Ivory, $4^7/_8$ x $6^3/_4$ in. (open)
     Lent by the Metropolitan Museum of Art (11.203)
     Rogers Fund, 1911

Another frequently employed juxtaposition in diptychs with two scenes was that of the Nativity and the Crucifixion. While the *Crucifixion* panel contains basically the same groupings as the similar scene in the Baltimore diptych (No. 76), the attitudes of the figures are now marked by mannered exaggeration. The *Nativity* panel contains many of the same elements as in the Detroit diptych (No. 74), with added emphasis given to the *Annunciation to the Shepherds,* situated in a schematic landscape in the background. This interest in depicting a bucolic scene peopled by antic shepherds parallels the beginning of an interest in representing nature and landscape, no matter how stylized, and reflects similar developments in the circle of Jean Pucelle (e.g., the Hours of Jeanne II de Navarre, Morand, 1962, pl. 18, b) and in the last quarter of the thirteenth century in the atelier of Jean Bondol (e.g., the Gotha Missal, Wixom, 1963, fig. 10).

Both scenes are situated beneath another common form of architectural frame, consisting of a cloisterlike arcade of three trefoil arches beneath crocheted and fleuronné gables. The complexity and precision of the carving and the tendency toward theatrical and mannered gestures relate this diptych to a group that Koechlin attributed to the Atelier of the Diptychs of the Passion (Koechlin, 1906, and also 1924, Vol. II, nos. 329, 808, 813), but as in the case of all Koechlin's categories, this group embraces a wide variety of styles throughout the century. Until the whole problem of the dating and attribution of Gothic ivories is restudied, we must be content with the observation that the particular combination of lively gestures, expressive physiognomy, and exquisite crispness of the carving is a translation in plastic terms of the qualities of Jean Pucelle's illuminations and therefore may be considered to date from the middle of the fourteenth century.

Literature: Metropolitan Museum, 1916, no. 116; Freeman, 1952, p. 110.

78   COFFRET*

French, end of 14th century
Beechwood, red lacquer, incised metal decoration, $2^3/_4$ x $5^1/_2$ x $4^1/_2$ in.
Lent by Paul Drey Gallery, New York

The small beechwood casket with decorative metal bars and clasp represents a fine example of a secular coffret, perhaps a marriage casket used by a noble lady to hold jewels and other oddments. The metal bands punctuating the sides and top of the casket are interrupted by flowers and are terminated by fleurs-de-lis, and between them are placed starlike metal rosettes. The metal guard running around the lid of the casket is incised with the inscription "Mon [drawing of a heart] Aves," standing for "Mon coeur à vous."

Exhibition: Tulsa, 1965, no. 119.

79   MARRIAGE CASKET: SCENES OF AMOROUS COUPLES*

English, 14th century
Ivory with silver clasps, $2^7/_8$ x $4^3/_8$ x $3^3/_8$ in.
Lent by the Museum of Fine Arts, Boston (64.1467)
Theodore Wilbour Fund in Memory of Charlotte Beebe Wilbour

Elaborate marriage caskets of carved ivory panels fastened with metal clasps provided ivory workers with the opportunity to represent a great variety of secular themes. Although it is true that some caskets were decorated with religious scenes of the type found on diptychs, triptychs, and tabernacles (see a casket in the Wernher Collection, Luton Hoo, England, in Natanson, 1951, no. 51, pls. 51–52), most of the jewel chests contain representations concerning the theme of courtly love. Some of these spell out incidents of a specific chivalric tale from the Arthurian romance, such as the stories of Launcelot, Tristam and Isolte, Gawain, and Percival, or scenes allegedly from the *Roman de la Rose* (see No. 81), or the cautionary tales of Aristotle and Phyllis or Virgil in the Basket (see Young, 1947, and Loomis, 1917). Often the decoration of such a casket was neither literary nor didactic, as may be seen in the charming Gothic coffret from Boston.

Said to have been in the possession of Lord Talbot, a judge at the trial of Joan of Arc at Rouen in 1430, the Boston casket contains representations of amorous couples beneath trefoiled and crocheted arches on the front, sides, back, and lid. The arcades are separated by silver bands with incised decoration. On the front panel we find a man and lady holding the incised lock with outstretched arms above a large ivory rosette. The two panels on the right end of the casket appear to have literary associations. One depicts the tryst of Tristam and Isolte by a fountain beneath the tree, from whose branches King Mark spies on them. In this episode from the Arthurian romances, the couple saw the King's reflection in the water and contrived to speak to each other so as to further deceive him. The second scene, of two lovers playing chess under a tree, may be a conventionalized representation derived from a famous chess game in the romance of Huon de Bourdeaux in which the knight played with a Saracen's daughter in order to win her hand and preserve his head (Cleveland, 1967, no. V–18).

In the other panels are the couples, all making gestures of endearment, some more proper than others. Most of the situations portrayed in the panels—such as the lover chucking his lady under the chin, the lady crowning the knight with a wreath, the giving of the heart (a visual representation of the engraved motto on the beechwood casket, No. 78), the *entretien* or conversation among lovers, and even the chess game—are all reflections of a strict code of behavior, a kind of ritual that had to be followed in emulation of the chivalric values embodied in the cult of courtly love.

These formal and symbolic gestures of endearment are found on a variety of secular objects such as mirror covers and combs and in the magnificent illustrations of the Manesse Liederhandschrift, a collection of German love lyrics of about 1315 (Heidelberg, Universitätsbibliothek, Cod. pal. germ. 848; see Paris, 1968, no. 262, for recent assessment and literature). The not-so-frequently-encountered gesture of a knight touching his lady's breast on the Boston example occurs on a casket in the Treasury of St. Ursula in Cologne (Koechlin, 1924, Vol. II, no. 1266), which also has the same device of a man and a woman holding the lock of the casket in their outstretched arms on the front panel. The rough-hewn quality of the carving seems closest to a coffret in the Victoria and Albert Museum said to be from northern France or Flanders (Koechlin, 1924, Vol. II, no. 1270).

Former Collection: Said to have belonged to Lord Talbot, a judge at the trial of Joan of Arc.

80   TOP OF A CASKET: JOUSTING SCENE*
French, 14th century
Ivory, $3^7/_8$ x $6^7/_8$ in.
Lent by the Metropolitan Museum of Art (17.190.256)
Gift of J. Pierpont Morgan, 1917

Armed combat on the field of honor became a necessary ritual proof of strength and courage for the knight who wished to win his lady's favors according to the chivalric code, and thus it was an appropriate subject for representation on the so-called Minnekatstchen, or marriage caskets, decorated with scenes of courtly love. The ivory panel from the Metropolitan Museum, divided into four panels, was probably once the lid of such a casket. In the center panel we see two knights jousting at full tilt before the crenellated wall of a castle, from which five onlookers watch the progress of the tournament. In each of the side panels an amorous couple converses beneath a tree, suggesting a wood or garden. But in the branches of each tree there sits a herald who is really part of the center scene, for his long horn projects into the adjacent panel and he appears to be blowing the call to charge for the knights below. The subject matter of the side panels thus differs from that found on most of the rare intact caskets of this sort that depict the Siege of the Castle of Love (see No. 81 and Young, 1947), but the representation of courting couples is entirely consistent with the theme of the tasks required and the rewards received according to the conventions of courtly love.

Former Collection: Oppenheim Collection, Paris.
Literature: Molinier, 1904, p. 32, no. 72; Koechlin, 1924, Vol. II, no. 1295; Loomis, 1917, pp. 19–27, fig. 1.

81   MIRROR BACK: SIEGE OF THE CASTLE OF LOVE*
French, Ile-de-France, *c.*1320–1350
Ivory, $4^1/_2$ x $4^1/_4$ in.
Lent by the Seattle Art Museum (Fr. 10.1)

A fitting complement to any noble lady's ivory casket adorned with such scenes as those observed above (Nos. 79 and 80) would be the carved ivory mirror back containing further representations of the same theme. Not unlike the ivory crozier head (No. 70), whose curvature was punctuated by projecting leaves, the round mirror backs were usually squared off at the corners with either leaves or exotic beasts such as the crouching wyverns on the mirror back from Seattle. The furious battle scene depicted here is not as serious as one might think at first glance. The castle is defended by damsels, who pelt the assailants with roses. A knight scaling the wall at the right is being assisted by one of the ladies, while the knight climbing the tree at the right turns over his sword in surrender, even before mounting the battlement, to a lady who is about to hurl a rose at him. Another knight on horseback below brings more ammunition, more roses in a basket. Two knights battle before the turreted gateway; one has three roses emblazoned on his shield and on the horse's trappings. The scene is thus one of the most popular allegorical representations on the theme of courtly love, whose origins have still not been fully explained (see Koechlin, 1921; Ross, 1928; Young, 1949; and others indicated below).

It has been said that this is an incident from the *Roman de la Rose,* (Wixom, 1967, p. 206), the allegorical poem concerning chivalric behavior begun by Guillaume de Lorris about 1230 and finished by Jean le Meun before 1270, which had a profound influence throughout the later Middle Ages. Certainly the theme is related, but the actual circumstances are far different, for in the poem Venus assists Love's Barons in an assault on the Castle of Jealousy and Shame (*Roman de la Rose,* Bks. 96 and 98). Beigbeder (1951 and 1965) has proposed that deeply symbolical and even religious overtones lie behind the imagery of some of these secular scenes. Although it is difficult to accept his thesis that the castle is really an evocation of the heavenly city of the Apocalypse, there is undoubtedly an interweaving of religious and secular iconography, stemming from such parallels as that between the cult of the Virgin and the exaltation of Love in the literature of the day. The closest example occurs in the fourth chapter of the German poem *Die Minneburg,* written about 1325–1350 (Loomis, 1919, p. 268; Neilson, 1899, pp. 123–126), where a youth is encouraged by the God of Love to attack a castle, the Freudenberg, inhabited by a lady. But for all the lack of clear literary parallels, numerous medieval pageants enacted in almost every detail the Siege of the Castle of Love as depicted on the Seattle ivory (Loomis, 1919).

The localization of these secular ivories still remains problematical. A similar mirror back in the Victoria and Albert Museum, (no. 9.72; Koechlin, 1924, II, no. 1002) and some related caskets are now considered to have originated in Cologne about 1340–1350 (Beigbeder, 1965, pp. 46, 48). But the Seattle example and an almost identical one formerly in the Sulzbach Collection in Paris (Koechlin, 1924, II, no. 1088) reveal a style that seems closer to what is still generally regarded as Parisian production at this period.

Former Collections: Baroness Lambert, Brussels; Baron Gustave de Rothschild, Paris.
Exhibitions: Cleveland, 1967, no. V–19.
Literature: Lee, 1949, pp. 192–193; Seattle, 1951, p. 216; Wixom, 1967, pp. 206–207, 369.

82 MIRROR BACK: AMOROUS COUPLES*
French, 14th century
Ivory, diameter 3³/₈ in.
Lent by the Walters Art Gallery, Baltimore (71.198)

Courtly love again provides the theme for the decoration of this mirror cover. Within a seven-lobed medallion inscribed within the circumference of the ivory disk are two pairs of lovers. On the left, the *rencontre,* or meeting, takes place, the man gently caressing the lady's cheek as she holds a flower (?). On the right, matters proceed with delicacy in the *entretien galante,* or conversation, each figure gesturing, the lady holding a dog in the crook of her arm. The tree dividing the roundel in two is symbolic of the garden, or perhaps wood, where the tryst is taking place, and the bird perched in its branches may be a falcon, which together with the dog may be taken for a symbol of the hunt, one of the frequently depicted occasions when a knight and his lady could contrive to exchange glances, say an unnoticed word to each other, or even slip away for a moment together from the rest of the hunting party. Perhaps the seven-lobed frame and the flower held by the lady on the left can both be taken for roses, the symbol of the quest for courtly love in the *Roman de la Rose.* The composition of the Baltimore example is similar to a mirror case formerly in the Homberg Collection, Paris (Koechlin, 1924, Vol. II, no. 1004).

83 MIRROR BACK: AMOROUS COUPLES
French, 14th century
Ivory, diameter 3¹/₂ in.
Lent by The Art Museum, Princeton University (54.61)

Two more scenes of courting couples, again repeating some of the situations found on the marriage casket (No. 79), decorate the mirror case from Princeton. Here, we find the crowning with a wreath and the giving of a flower, apparently preliminary gestures before mounting the stairs into the castle. Both scenes take place before a crenellated wall and are separated by what appears to be either a crudely wrought turret or an awkwardly rendered tree trunk, whose foliage spreads out above the crenellations. Perhaps this wall can be construed as the castle built around the Rose by Jealousy in the *Roman de la Rose* (ll. 3797–4058) with its leaves showing above, and perhaps can thus be considered as a veritable Castle of Love (No. 81).

Literature: Record of the Art Museum, Princeton University, XIV, no. 1 (1955), 19.

84 COMB: PREPARATION FOR THE JOUST AND THE JOUST*
French?, 15th century
Ivory, 4⁷/₈ x 5³/₄ in.
Lent by Paul Drey Gallery, New York

Although this ivory comb probably dates from the fifteenth century, the theme of its decoration warrants its inclusion with the other secular ivories containing scenes of courtly love. One side depicts a person bathing; a handmaiden pours water into the tub from a pitcher, and a stylized flower, perhaps a rose, is growing out of the tub. The second portion of the scene shows the person after bathing, kneeling and praying at the foot of a bed. On the reverse side, two knights are shown jousting, their winged helms and the fluttering skirts of their caparisoned horses trailing behind. A stylized rose vine with palmettelike leaves climbs through the vertical borders at each end of the comb, and the whole ensemble is enclosed by a spiral rope-twist border.

Both sides together represent the specific ritual through which each knight went the night before his day on the lists: the ritual cleansing or bath, which here involves the rose as a reminder of the true knight's chivalric goal, the quest if not the attainment of his lady's favors, and then the all-night vigil before the tournament.

The crosshatched background, the trailing rose vine and palmette decoration, and even the harsh carving of the figures exemplified in this comb are highly representative of a group of secular ivories believed to have been carved in France in the fifteenth century (see a casket lid and a comb in the Victoria and Albert Museum: Tardy, 1966, p. 101, and Koechlin, 1924, Vol. II, no. 1153). A related comb, but with different foliate decoration, and said to be either French or northern Italian from about 1400, is in the Kofler-Truniger Collection in Lucerne (Schnitzler, 1964, no. S. 128). Though lacking in comparable elegance and sophistication, the comb also reflects the style of a mirror case in Baltimore (Walters Art Gallery 71.107: Baltimore, 1962, no. 122) now considered to be Italian, possibly Venetian. Perhaps when more research has been done on this group, it will turn out that a non-French, possibly northern Italian attribution for these ivories will be more nearly correct.

Exhibition: Binghamton, 1968, no. 21.

85   COMB*
         French, late 15th century
         Boxwood, 7 x 5 in.
         Lent by the Detroit Institute of Arts (47.96)
         Gift of Mrs. Lilian Henkel Haas

Toward the end of the Middle Ages, boxwood began to replace ivory as a material for the carving of statuettes, miniature devotional objects, and secular items such as combs. Close-grained, dense, and durable, boxwood permitted carvers to achieve a degree of virtuosity unobtainable in ivory. The Late Gothic comb from Detroit attests to the quality and complexity of decoration that a skilled craftsman could evoke from the material. As in the case of the ivory comb (No. 84), the boxwood example has two rows of teeth, one fine and the other larger and more widely spaced. Intricate, pierced Gothic tracery forming lancets and roundels transforms the remainder of the object into a lacy filigree, evocative of careful wrought ironwork. The patterns are symmetrically arranged, both horizontally and vertically, around the central rosettelike medallion, which contains an inscription in Gothic letters: "de bon [coeur] te [or je] done." It is possible that the words refer to the gift of the comb by someone, possibly a man, to a lady, as in the inscription on the beechwood Gothic coffret (No. 78). On the other hand, they may refer to the consecration of nuns, for a similar comb now in Philadelphia contains the words "deo un [coeur] le done" (Weinberger, 1941, no. 247) and could, therefore, be a liturgical comb used in the consecration ceremonies. The former seems more probable, however, for there are two sliding panels on the back which cover circular depressions that may have been used to contain pomade.

Former Collection: Henry Chauncey, New York.

86   COMB*
French, late 15th century
Boxwood, $7^5/_8$ x $5^1/_2$ in.
Lent by Francis Waring Robinson, Detroit

In comparison with No. 85, a finer and more regular articulation of the two rows of teeth and a denser pattern of ajouré, or pierced, decoration characterize this late fifteenth-century boxwood comb. The repetitive, starlike penetrations dominate the design, and where they are interrupted by the overlapping roundels or completely invaded by them in the central panel, the structure dissolves in a filigree of the utmost delicacy. Lancet forms, like flamboyant Gothic stained-glass windows, accentuate the corners. The inscription in Gothic letters continues on both faces of the comb: "Pour vour / servir." A large number of similar combs are preserved both in the United States and abroad. Since the majority of them have inscriptions in French, it seems possible that most of them were produced in France.

Former Collections: Charles Tyson Yerkes, New York (sale, April 13, 1910, cat. no. 463); William Randolph Hearst, New York.

87   QUATREFOIL MEDALLIONS: CHRIST, ST. PETER
Italian, Tuscany?, *c.*1375
Champlevé enamel on copper, diameter $2^7/_8$ in.
Lent by the Walters Art Gallery, Baltimore (44.460 and 44.449)

The two quatrefoil champlevé medallions with the busts of Christ and St. Peter are from a set of thirteen, now in the Walters Art Gallery, that originally adorned an altarcloth. Verdier has pointed out that the set is probably missing three medallions of the Evangelists and that Luke, Matthew, Mark, and John, therefore, would have been represented twice, with different but appropriate attributes (Baltimore, 1962, no. 135). Thus St. John is shown with both a chalice as an apostle and with a book as an Evangelist. In the present examples, Christ is depicted with a crossed halo, holding a book and making a gesture of benediction, and the tonsured St. Peter is shown also holding a book as well as a key. The figures are executed in reserve, or on the actual surface of the copper itself, which has been gilt and into which have been scratched the massed lines delineating features and drapery folds. These lines have been filled with dark blue enamel, contrasting with the dull blue enamel of the ground. The corners of the design are punctuated by stylized leaves in gilt reserve set off against a red enamel ground.

According to Verdier (in Baltimore, 1962, no. 135), the technique and effect of these medallions reflects the Italian assimilation in the region of Tuscany of a style of metalwork that was prevalent around Vienna and the Austrian regions of the Upper Rhine. Verdier deems the style of draughtsmanship not unworthy of the Florentine goldsmith Pietro di Leonardo, active about 1360; certainly the strength and vigor of the figures carries the same intensity of religious fervor and some of the hieratic quality evident in Florentine art in the latter half of the fourteenth century, notably in the followers of Andrea Orcagna.

Exhibition: Baltimore, 1962, no. 135.

88 CANDLEHOLDER: KNEELING MAN*
German, early 15th century
Brass, 9³/₄ x 5¹/₈ in.
Lent by Duke University
Brummer Collection

Kneeling on a triangular platform supported by three human feet, the bearded man clothed in a close-fitting tunic and cowl holds a candle socket in his left hand. The upraised right hand held an object that is now missing. Moeller has related this magnificent figured candleholder to other examples in Boston and Providence, Rhode Island, and to a group of related works published by Falke and Meyer (Moeller, 1967, p. 80; Falke and Meyer, 1935, Vol. I, no. 527, pl. 213 and p. 88), all of which are attributed to Germany in the fifteenth century. Moeller quite rightly assigns the Duke candleholder to the early fifteenth century. The style of the costume reflects the trend of closely fitting garments and hour-glass figures that prevailed from about the 1370's until the early years of the fifteenth century. Such a costume made its appearance in German metalwork by about 1380 in the "Brünnen-Hansel" of the Nürnberg Fountain (Vienna, 1962, no. 396, pl. 160).

Former Collection: Ernst Brummer.
Exhibition: Raleigh, 1967, no. 31.
Literature: Moeller, 1967, pp. 80–81, no. 31, fig. 44.

89 THE LORD REPRIMANDING ADAM AND EVE*

Franco-Italian or Lombard, late 14th century

Alabaster with traces of polychrome, 20$^{1}/_{4}$ x 25$^{3}/_{4}$ in.

Lent by the M. H. de Young Memorial Museum, San Francisco

Adam and Eve stand sheepishly clutching fig leaves in their new-found modesty as the Lord berates them for disobeying Him and eating the apple of the tree of knowledge. The serpent coils around a tree between Adam and Eve, and a luxurious grove provides the backdrop of the Garden of Eden.

The deeply carved and polychromed alabaster panel is thought to be of Franco-Italian origin. It may be possible to localize it a bit more precisely. The squatness and solidity of the figures and the manner of treating the drapery in curving folds around the figure of God reflect the style of Bonino da Campione (active 1357–1388) and an unknown Lombard artist of about 1360, influenced by him, who was responsible for the altar table reliefs in the parochial church at Carpiano (see Milan, 1958, nos. 32 and 33–35, and Milan, 1959, pls. 14–15). Further associations with the art of Lombardy may be seen in the recurrence of facial types with high cheekbones, small but finely articulated eyes, smooth modeling, and, in the case of Eve, a rather mousey expression similar to those found in the miniatures and paintings attributed to Michelino da Besozzo. Moreover, the representation of the trees in the background, with foliage built up of an accumulation of large, stylized leaves, reflects the similar device found in the Lombard manuscripts of the *Tacuinum Sanitatis* of the end of the fourteenth century (see Vienna, Osterreichische Nationalbibliothek, MS. S.N.2644: Milan, 1959, pl. XVII). It should be added that there is also a similarity between the figures of the San Francisco relief and those of two prophets executed for Milan Cathedral about 1400, thought to be by a Burgundian artist in the style of André Beauneveu (Milan, 1958, nos. 120–121, pl. 39). But the style of the San Francisco relief appears to fall between that of the works by Bonino da Campione and his circle and that of the "Burgundian" Milan prophets and may be considered to reflect the style of carving in Lombardy at the moment of the fusion of French and Italian elements in the creation of the "International Style" of about 1400.

Exhibition: New York, *Pictures on Exhibit* (New York, 1951), p. 41, illus.
Literature: Art Quarterly, XXIII (1960), 91, illus.

90 STATUETTES: MOURNING VIRGIN AND ST. JOHN*

French, Burgundy?, *c.*1400

Ivory, 4$^{1}/_{8}$ and 4 in.

Lent by the Museum of Fine Arts, Boston (49.486–7)

William F. Warden Fund

The two ivory statuettes, one of the mourning Virgin and the other of the praying St. John, are from a small Crucifixion group of which the central portion, Christ on the Cross, is now missing. Both statuettes reflect the style of the late fourteenth and early fifteenth centuries, possibly in eastern France under the influence of developments in Burgundy. The treatment of the ample drapery sweeping around and across the front of the figure seems to prefigure the more voluminous and substantial style manifested by Claus Sluter and his followers at Dijon in the first decade of the fifteenth century. But the delicacy and refinement of the carving, no doubt due to the small, intimate scale, and the use of the multiple, curvilinear hems evident on the statuette of the Virgin are most evocative of the meticulous figures and diaphanous drapery style current among manuscript illuminators supported by the Duke of Berry, notably the so-called "Imitator of the Parement Master" active in the Milan Hours of about 1405–1409 (Turin, Museo Civico; see Meiss, 1967, Vol. II, figs. 41–43, 45).

91   PROPHET*
      French, Burgundy, c.1400
      Limestone, 27$^1/_2$ in.
      Lent by the Museum of Fine Arts, Boston (39.760)
      Harriet Otis Cruft Fund

The impact of the art of Claus Sluter on French sculpture in the first half of the fifteenth century can be clearly seen in this monumental image of a prophet. Sluter was a Dutch artist who executed the sculptures for the portal and pedestal of a Calvary, now known as the Well of Moses, for the Carthusian Monastery of Champmol near Dijon between 1397 and 1405. He infused into French sculpture a new intense realism in the physiognomies and characterizations of his figures and a new overwhelming sense of presence, of a superhuman breadth and massiveness, by clothing them in voluminous and heavily activated draperies. The gnarled visage of the Boston prophet, its astonishing, aged face creased and wrinkled by time, reveals the merciless observation that is evident in Sluter's works and that also carries over into Flemish painting of the fifteenth century. But the Boston figure is not as solidly and broadly conceived as the figure of the Well of Moses. Although the tapering, swaying effect of its pose may be exaggerated by the damage to the bottom of the statue, which has destroyed the feet, the looping folds of the ample garment sweep around the form and lend it an uplifting vitality. These draperies are not as heavy and voluminous as those by Sluter and his close followers (see a similar-size statue of St. John the Baptist at the Morgan Library, Baltimore, 1962, no. 83, pl. LXXXVI) or two statues from Poligny in the Metropolitan Museum (Müller, 1966, pls. 56a and b). Rather, they manifest a continuing penchant for swinging curves and an elegant silhouette that is analogous to the effects we have just observed in the small ivory statuettes (No. 90). In place of Sluter's intense, almost daemonic characterizations, the Boston prophet seems more introspective and contemplative as he peers out of the shadows of the enveloping cowl at a book (the book and left forearm are now missing). Although the more attenuated proportions and swaying profile are reminiscent of an earlier phase of sculpture exemplified by the works of André Beauneveu, the meticulous realism of the features and the powerful compositional accents of the drapery suggest a source close to the work of Claus Sluter, perhaps even in his workshop.

92 PAIR OF STATUETTES: TWO BISHOPS*
Dutch, Utrecht?, c.1500
Wood, 7 in. and $6^7/8$ in.
Lent by Michael Hall Fine Arts, Inc., New York

The two exquisitely carved statuettes of bishops are shown clothed in their vestments and carrying books, presumably Bibles. Both are mitered, but one wears the triangular chasuble over the closely fitting skirtlike tunicle and the flowing undergarment, or alb; the other wears a broad, tassle-edged dalmatic over the alb. The sturdy proportions of the figures and the rugged carving of the features are representative of the wooden sculptures produced in the northern Lowlands, the area that is now Holland, about the beginning of the sixteenth century.

This Dutch attribution is borne out by the close similarity of these two statuettes to two somewhat larger ones reputed to be in the Frederiks Collection in 'S-Gravenhage (Bouvy, 1957, pl. 164, figs. a and b). These are two statuettes from a set of four representing the four fathers of the Church, St. Ambrose, St. Augustine, St. Gregory, and St. Jerome, which Bouvy believes are probably from Utrecht Cathedral and may date from the first decade of the sixteenth century (1957, p. 148). Our statuettes are approximately one quarter the size of the Frederiks examples, and they lack their fine degree of individualization in the features, but in every other respect almost identical stylistic conventions are employed in both sets. Moreover, the similarities are such that one can identify the present statuettes with a reasonable amount of certainty. The bishop wearing a chasuble holds a closed book in his left hand and holds his right hand up as though to grasp a bishop's crozier. The Frederiks statue of St. Ambrose is virtually identical: the chasuble, the closed book, and the upheld right hand holding a short tubular object. This is probably the handle of a scourge, one of the attributes of St. Ambrose, who is credited with driving the Arians out of Italy. St. Ambrose can be shown holding either a crozier or a scourge, and in view of the other striking compositional and stylistic similarities, our statue is probably this bishop-saint. The second statuette, the bishop wearing the dalmatic and holding an open book in his left hand, has the right hand upraised. Again, vestments and pose are identical to the Frederiks statue of St. Augustine, who in the latter example appears to grasp the flaming heart, symbol of his great piety, and holds a small building tucked in the crook of his arm, perhaps symbolic of his great work, the *City of God*. In the palm of our statue is a rounded hollow, evidence that he also held something spherical, possibly the flaming heart, but there is no evidence of the building as in the larger statue. Although the evidence is less conclusive, the striking similarity with the Frederiks St. Augustine suggests that he was the father of the Church represented in the present example. On the basis of the close correspondences between the Augustine and Ambrose statues from Utrecht Cathedral and our pair of statuettes, it seems likely that both sets were carved at about the same time and quite possibly in the same workshop.

93   STANDING VIRGIN AND CHILD*
     Dutch, Utrecht or Province of Holland?, late 15th or early 16th century
     Oak, 25$^{1}/_{2}$ x 10$^{1}/_{2}$ in.
     Lent by the Philadelphia Museum of Art ('23–23–84)
     Charles F. Williams Collection

The standing Virgin is crowned and clothed in an ample cloak, which envelops her in a myriad of restless, curving loops and folds. Long, curling tresses cascade down over her shoulders, reaching as far as her elbows. She holds the Christ child in the crook of her right arm and tenderly caresses his foot with her left hand. Perhaps the gesture is one of humility, even though she is crowned Queen of Heaven, to prefigure not only the Magdalene's washing of Christ's feet but also Christ's later washing of the feet of the apostles. The curly-headed infant holds a clump of grapes, symbolic of the wine of the Eucharist and of his sacrifice on the Cross.

The statue is difficult to localize exactly, but it appears to resemble in a general way a Madonna and Child in the Aartsbisschoppelijk Museum in Utrecht that was believed to have been produced in the Province of Holland in the northern Netherlands about 1500 (Utrecht, 1962, no. 111, fig. 47). There is an analogous treatment of the hair of both Madonna and Child, and a similar directionless agitation of the drapery folds. Both Virgins wear a similar form of clothing, a square-cut bodice under which appears the *V*-shaped neck of the undergarment, which helps to confirm an approximate date of 1500–1520 (see Utrecht, 1962, no. 115, fig. 43). The Utrecht statue is attributed to Holland with Brabant influence, or in other words with influences from the area of the southern Lowlands or Flanders, which is present-day Belgium. Indeed, some of the soft generalization of the features of the Utrecht statue, notably the fleshy face and high-domed forehead reflect a style normally considered to be Flemish. Perhaps the differences between this and our example from Philadelphia, in which the face is more elongated and the features are more exaggerated, almost caricatural, indicate the work of a Dutch artist who was less prone to Flemish influences.

Exhibition: Philadelphia, 1966.

94 STATUETTE OF VIRGIN AND CHILD*

Flemish, Malines?, late 15th century
Bronze, 10³/₈ in.
Lent by the Walters Art Gallery, Baltimore (53.38)

The standing Virgin, clothed in an ample, flowing cloak over a more tightly fitting tunic, is holding the Christ Child, nude from the waist down, diagonally across her body. The infant twists forward and plays with a rosary, from which hangs a large spherical pendant. As in the case of so many other medieval representations of the Madonna and Child, the statuette thus embodies a prefiguration of the Passion of Christ and of the worship of the Virgin herself. The rosary is a reference to the latter, recalling to the mind of the devout spectator the recitation of the prayers and meditations on the events of both their lives.

The distinctive characteristics of the Baltimore statuette, with the small, rounded head, the high-domed forehead, the accentuated eyes, the sweet expression, and the broad, apronlike effect of the drapery, relates it to numerous small statues that were made in Malines in the latter third of the fifteenth century and into the early decades of the sixteenth century. Of the numerous examples that have been published (Borchgrave d'Altena, 1959, and Godenne, 1958), many have the city mark of Malines, an M or four parallel slashes. Usually these statuettes were of polychromed wood. The bronze Baltimore statuette presents an unusual variation in material, though it is almost identical in form, composition, and style with statuettes in Marseilles and Berlin (see Godenne, 1958, Vol. I, pl. 6, and 1959, Vol. II, pl. 59).

95 ANNUNCIATE VIRGIN*

Flemish, Province of Brabant, Brussels?, last quarter of 15th century
Wood, 47 x 32 in.
Lent by Professor and Mrs. Rudolph B. Schlesinger, Ithaca, New York

The arresting life-size statue of the Virgin kneeling at a prie-dieu is most probably from an Annunciation group of which the angel is now missing. Mary has been startled as she was turning the page of the book before her, and recoiling and turning slightly to the side, she lifts her hand in surprise.

The contemplative motif of Mary reading or praying at the moment when the Angel Gabriel intrudes to give her the news of the coming birth of Christ was a favorite one throughout Europe during the Gothic period, but this charming and impressive statue most clearly reflects the mood and the style of the *Annunciation* as represented in fifteenth-century Flemish paintings. The sweet, simplified, serene features, the characteristic high-domed forehead, the delicate modeling of the eyelids, and the subtle definition of the eyebrows reflect analogous features in paintings from Jan van Eyck's Rolin Madonna of about 1435 (Panofsky, 1953, Vol. II, fig. 246) to the *grisaille* Annunciation on the outer panels of the Portinari Altarpiece by Hugo van der Goes of about 1475 (Panofsky, 1953, Vol. II, fig. 465). Moreover, the treatment of the drapery, with the cloak falling in straight, vertical, and somewhat flattened folds from the shoulders and then cascading about the feet in a broad pyramidal mass of angular, overlapping planes and crinkled ridges, manifests the same conventions employed in Flemish paintings of the period. It was not uncommon for sculptors to emulate the figure types, poses, and even entire compositions of such artists as Roger van der Weyden; a striking example is the dramatic *Lamentation* relief in Detroit, which was copied from Roger's painting now in the Prado (cf. Verhaegen, 1962). In fact, a remarkably similar representation of the Virgin, both in style and in posture, occurs in a panel of the *Annunciation* by Roger in the Louvre (Panofsky, 1953, Vol. II, fig. 310): the Virgin is kneeling at a prie-dieu and has raised her hand in surprise.

But, at this point, we must note an important difference. The Weyden Virgin is shown in the act of turning around to look over her shoulder at the Angel, who is approaching from behind or from the left. Our statue, on the other hand, which is a $^3/_4$ relief and hollowed out in back so that it must be seen from a profile view, shows the Virgin directing her attention over the prie-dieu to the right toward the Angel, who must be approaching her from the front. Yet if we look at other examples of the *Annunciation* in Flemish Art, we find that it is the composition used by Roger that occurs on the outer panels of the Ghent Altarpiece, in the main panel of the Mérode Altarpiece, and in panels by Petrus Christus, Dirc Bouts, and their followers. Curiously, in two important examples where the Angel approaches from the right, one by a follower of Roger on the outer panels of his Bladelin Altarpiece and the other on the outer panels of Hugo's Portinari Altarpiece (Panofsky, 1953, Vol. II, figs. 335 and 461), the entire composition has been reversed, and the Virgin still turns away from her book to face Gabriel, who is behind her. The same type of composition is frequently found in sculpture. In a number of small wooden reliefs of the *Annunciation*, one of about 1500 in the Musées Royaux in Brussels (Detroit, 1960, no. 99), another of about 1500–1510 in the Busch-Reisinger Museum in Cambridge, Massachusetts (Kuhn, 1965, no. 24), and a third of about 1490 still in place in a retable in the Musée Communale in Brussels (Borchgrave d'Altena, 1947, pls. XLIX and L), we find the Virgin turning to face the Angel on the left. Thus it appears that a direct confrontation between Mary and the Angel with the latter situated at the right, which in this case may have been used because of the size of this statue or as a reflection of the artist's originality, is a relatively unusual composition.

This variation becomes even more extraordinary when we consider that our kneeling Virgin is stylistically related to those reliefs cited above. The treatment of the features, the drapery, and the hair, falling in coarse, wavy tresses, resembles most closely those of the Cambridge *Annunciation*, which is considered to be of Brabant origin (Kuhn, 1965, no. 24) and in a more general way approximates the style of the two Brussels *Annunciations* as well as the effect of a Virgin and Child in the Louvre that has the Brussels' city mark and that is considered to date from 1490–1500 (Pradel, 1947, pl. 9).

Localization of the Annunciate Virgin should be made easily and with certainty, for the statue bears what appear to be two marks, one a punch mark and the other a series of parallel and right-angle lines gouged into the wood. The punch mark is extremely difficult to read; it unfortunately seems to be neither the mallet mark nor the wafflelike *poinçon* of the city of Brussels, nor is it the hand mark of the city of Antwerp. It appears rather as a kind of stylized plant with the stalk sprouting from a ground line and two sets of leaves symmetrically arranged on each side. It resembles slightly the fleuronné mark that Destrée published as being on a charming statue of the Magdalene, now in the Musées Royaux in Brussels, and that also has an imperfect *poinçon de maillet* of the city of Brussels (Destrée, 1891, pp. 64–65; see also Detroit, 1960, p. 247, no. 80). The second mark, the *marque à la gouge,* could possibly be a control mark for the quality of the wood or the carver's own mark (cf. those of Pierre Cornielis and another anonymous artist illustrated in Doorslaer, 1933, pp. 173 and 174). It should also be noted that it bears a general resemblance to the four parallel slashes of the city of Malines (especially as recorded on a small statuette now at Beaune: Godenne, 1958, Vol. I, no. 1), but the scale and style of the Virgin appears to rule out the possibility of its originating in a town that specialized in small, elegantly costumed, mannered statuettes at the end of the fifteenth century. It is hoped that further research concerning the marks and the relationship of this magnificent statue with other examples of Flemish sculpture will one day yield more exact information about its origin and context.

96   MOURNING VIRGIN
     English, last half of 15th century
     Bath stone, 25 in.
     Lent by Michael Hall Fine Arts, Inc., New York

Though greatly damaged and abraded, this moving statue of the sorrowing Virgin, presumably from a Crucifixion group, still imparts a sensitive portrayal of self-contained emotion and monumental dignity. She stands quietly, her head inclined forward under the enveloping hood of her mantle, her right hand across her waist and her left clutching a gathering of the drapery. The simple silhouette, the broadly curving folds, and the pervading effect of composure that dominates the statue evoke the standing Virgins in the less emotional representations of the Crucifixion by Roger van der Weyden and his followers—for example, the standing figure of a mourner in the left panel of the Vienna Triptych and in the Cambrai Altarpiece in Madrid (Friedländer, 1967, Vol. II, pls. 18 and 67). No doubt such similarities contributed to a former attribution of this statue to Flanders (Tulsa, 1965, no. 83), but the stone appears to be English in origin, perhaps Bath stone, although this has not been proved by analysis. It would have been entirely possible for it to have been carved in England, for there appears to have been a strong Flemish influence in the British Isles at the end of the fifteenth century, as the exquisitely carved fragment of a Madonna and Child at Winchester attests (Stone, 1955, p. 225 and fig. 184). The wholesale destruction and defacement of so many medieval English sculptures may prevent us from ever establishing with certainty the origin of the Mourning Virgin, but on the basis of material and a general affinity of style with the Winchester Virgin, it is possible to suggest that it may have been carved in England in the latter half of the century by an artist reflecting Flemish influences.

Exhibitions: Tulsa, 1965, no. 83; Nelson Art Gallery, Kansas City, Dec. 1967–Jan. 1968.

97   ALABASTER RELIEF: TREE OF JESSE
     English, school of Nottingham, *c*.1430–1440
     Alabaster, with traces of polychrome, 26 x 9 in.
     Lent by the Philadelphia Museum of Art ('45–25–108)
     The George Grey Barnard Collection

Although many alabaster reliefs that originally were arranged in rows to form large and elaborate retables or altarpieces have survived to the present day, the Philadelphia panel possesses a number of unusual characteristics. Only two other reliefs are known that depict the same subject, the Tree of Jesse, one at Hadleigh in Suffolk, England (cf. Nelson, 1917, pl. 1) and a second at Vernon near Rouen in France (cf. Tavender, 1949, pl. 8). The theme is that of a literal representation of the genealogy of Christ from Jesse, the father of David, to the personage of the Virgin and Child, based on a passage in the prophecy of Isaiah (XI, 1): "And there shall come forth a rod out of the root of Jesse, and a flower shall rise up out of his root. And the spirit of the Lord shall rest upon him." Thus the root of the flowering branch springing from the chest of Jesse signifies the lineage of the Old Testament kings, the branch symbolizes the Virgin, who is here seated in the top center of the panel, and the flower which she bears signifies her son, Christ (cf. Mâle, 1958, pp. 165–168). This representation became increasingly popular in the late twelfth century and into the thirteenth century as part of the elaborate iconography that grew up in connection with the popular cult of the Virgin in the Gothic period. For this reason, it is supposed that the present panel was part of a large altarpiece dedicated to the Virgin and was accompanied by representations of the Annunciation (this companion piece is now in the Philadelphia Museum of Art; see Tavender, 1955, p. 66, no. 15), the Nativity, the Assumption of the Virgin, and possibly the Visitation or the Purification of the Virgin (Tavender, 1955, p. 66, no. 16).

The production of alabaster panels for retables became a veritable industry in England in the fifteenth century, particularly in the region around Nottingham (cf. Stone, 1955, p. 180; Cheetham, 1962, and Richard H. Randall, 1966). The panels were virtually mass-produced, which accounts for the increasingly high degree of standardization in composition and iconography. The easily workable quality of the stone permitted craftsmen to carve intricate groupings of figures such as the present example, and the richness of effect was further enhanced by the application of polychrome and gilt as well as by the total visual impression of the serried ranks of these reliefs in a large altarpiece.

Given the degree of uniformity of theme and format, therefore, it is even more remarkable to find the unusual subject of the Tree of Jesse. The panel belongs to a group in which an increased use of undercutting for decorative effect is combined with the employment of embattled or crenellated canopies projecting above the scene and a stagelike canted platform protruding at the bottom (cf. Nelson, 1918). In the Philadelphia panel, however, the bayed platform at the bottom is both crenellated and penetrated by quatrefoil tracery, while there is no canopy above. Presumably the effect of the altarpiece from which the Jesse Tree relief came would have looked something like the alabaster retable from St.-Germain d'Auxerre, now in the Museum at Compiègne in France, which employs both traceried canopies and platforms (cf. Prior and Gardner, 1904, p. 467, fig. 538, and Tavender, 1949, pl. 2). Although the Compiègne retable was probably made later, about 1480, and is certainly more elaborate in its conception, perhaps we may be justified in suggesting that both Philadelphia panels (the *Tree of Jesse* and the *Annunciation*) that have similar platforms may also have had embattled and possibly traceried canopies. The broken and irregular edges at the tops of both reliefs tend to support this thesis.

Former Collection: George Grey Barnard.
Literature: Weinberger, 1941, p. 22, no. 108, pl. XXXI; Tavender, 1949, p. 402; Tavender, 1955, p. 66, no. 16, pl. 2.

98   RELIEF: PRESENTATION OF THE VIRGIN AT THE TEMPLE
     German, *c.*1480
     Wood, traces of gesso and polychrome, 16 x 14¼ in.
     Lent by the Philadelphia Museum of Art ('23–23–73)
     Charles F. Williams Collection

The young girl, Mary, mounts a steep flight of stairs to the portal of the temple where the high priest, wearing a bishop's miter and holding an open book, awaits her. Joachim holds a necklace or perhaps a rosary and Anna holds a book as they stand behind the Virgin, and a patriarchal figure watches from the left side. The incident, which fulfills the vow of Anna that if she should have a child it would be dedicated to the Lord in the Holy Temple, is derived from the thirteenth-century Golden Legend of Jacobus de Voragine, which in turn draws from a number of earlier, apocryphal gospels. The motif of the high stairway leading up to the temple seems to have been invented by Giotto in his frescoes in the Arena Chapel at the beginning of the fourteenth century, but by the fifteenth century it had gained considerable popularity throughout Europe. In this relief the scene is interpreted with contemporary costumes and setting: the temple is a Gothic church and the high priest is in the guise of a bishop. These contemporary details imply that the Presentation of the Virgin at the Temple is in effect a parallel to the Virgin's reception into the Christian church. The stocky proportions, the heavy, serious facial types, and the manner of treating the drapery are indicative of a provincial artist active in the Lower Rhine region of Germany toward the end of the fifteenth century. An analogous weightiness and style are evident in a Holy Family group in Berlin considered to be Lower Rhenish, about 1500 (Demmler, 1930, p. 314, no. 482).

99 THE CIRCUMCISION

Flemish, Antwerp, c.1520–1540
Oak, traces of polychrome, 13³/₄ x 12¹/₄ in.
Lent by the Philadelphia Museum of Art ('23–23–86)
Charles F. Williams Collection

Positively bursting with elegantly dressed spectators crowding around the high altar, this relief of the Circumcision is more secular than religious in feeling. A tonsured priest in full vestments and wearing a pair of spectacles perched on the end of his nose bends over the Infant to make the operation, while the buxom Virgin holds the Child still. Two small, winged angels appear beneath the altar with a cauldron of water and lift a sponge to cleanse the wound. A monkey-faced gentleman in a wide-brimmed hat with a great, looping chin strap and a pleated, knotted cape stands opposite the priest; an assortment of young women in fanciful headdresses press in upon the scene. Though not a work of the highest quality, the intricacy of the carving and the play of light and shadow over the forms imply the hubbub of chatter that must be going on. Yet by boldly stating the volumes of the priest and the richly dressed onlooker, by foreshortening the altartop and placing the angels as *repoussoirs* before it, and by skillfully manipulating the spaces between the figures, the artist has managed to suggest an effective, convincing spatial recession.

This group of figures, which would have fitted within a compartment or *huche* of a large, intricately sculpted retable, is typical in its subject matter and its presumed context of a large number of sculpted and painted altars produced in Antwerp in the sixteenth century. A favorite theme in Antwerp was that of the Adoration of the Magi, which was frequently represented in the central panel of both painted and sculpted retables, and even when the central theme concerned the Crucifixion and incidents of the Passion, there were often compartments along the predella that contained scenes related to the Nativity (cf. Borchgrave d'Altena, 1957, *passim*). Certainly the Adoration of the Magi scenes, and sometimes the Circumcision and the Presentation at the Temple (e.g. the Coesfeld Retable, Borchgrave d'Altena,

1957, figs. 31–32), provided the excuse for painter and sculptor alike to exercise his talent for creating bizarre costumes, crowds of widely differentiated characters, a variety of strikingly mannered poses, and a wealth of intricate detail. Our relief, in which the details of the priest's vestments, the tassels hanging from his cape, the purse and other objects hanging from his belt, the eyeglasses, the cauldron of water, are rendered with a great delight and fascination in the variety of material things, emulates this Antwerp tradition. Although no exact counterparts to the Philadelphia relief have as yet been found, it reflects in a crude way the caricatural and mannered style found in the retables of Coesfeld of about 1520 and of Haltern of about 1510–1515 (Borchgrave d'Altena, 1957, figs. 31–32, 61–68).

100 VIRGIN AND CHILD; SALVATOR MUNDI
German, lower Franconia, Wurzburg?, c.1510
Fruitwood, 7 in.
Lent by Paul Drey Galleries, New York

This extraordinary statuette, with two figures placed back to back, has been shown by Justus Bier to be derived from two larger works by Tilman Riemenschneider both dating from about 1510. According to Bier, the figure of the Salvator Mundi, Christ as Savior, holding an orb and making a blessing, is derived from the nearly identical figure from the high altar of Wurzburg Cathedral, which is now in the parish church at Biebelreid. The Virgin and Child are adapted from a similar statue now in the Kunsthistorische Museum in Vienna (Bier, 1962, p. 68). The fruitwood statuette may have been used, as Bier suggests, either as a model for a bronze casting or as the crowning figure of a staff, meant to be "carried above the heads of the pilgrims in a religious procession." It is evident from the more schematic treatment of the draperies and compacted features that this curious statuette is not by Riemenschneider's hand, but it seems likely that it was carved by someone who was familiar with the Master's Wurzburg productions.

Former Collection: Otto Bernheimer, Munich.
Exhibition: Raleigh, 1962, no. XX.
Literature: A. Weinmüller, sale catalogue 83, Auction 75, no. 812; Bier, 1962, p. 68.

101 ST. ROCH AND THE ANGEL*
German, Franconia?, c.1500–1510
Lindenwood, 28⁷/₈ in.
Lent by the Metropolitan Museum of Art (60.126)
The Cloisters Collection

St. Roch, patron saint of the sick and the poor, is shown here in one of the legendary incidents concerning his life. Presumably, while he was on a pilgrimage to Rome, an epidemic of the plague broke out, and he delayed his travels to help tend to the sick. He became ill with the disease himself, but was cared for by a dog who brought him bread and by an angel who came to cure him. In some representations of the Saint we find him depicted with both the dog and the angel (e.g., Ginderich parish church: Bouvy, 1947, fig. 200) or with just the dog (e.g., Kranenburg parish church: Bouvy, 1947, fig. 199) or with just the angel rubbing salve on a sore on his leg, as in the present example.

The extraordinarily fine articulation of the features, the fine crinkles around the eyes, the emaciation of the face, and the sorrowful expression, and above all the sympathetic and penetrating presentation of the Saint reflects the achievement of Tilman Riemenschneider in a statue of St. Mark in Berlin (cf. Gerstenberg, 1962, fig. 28). But the emphasis on the slashing diagonal drapery folds in the Cloisters piece, the lack of crispness and electric charge in the crinkled drapery, and the fat, flaccid face of the angel preclude Riemenschneider's own participation in the work. Yet the unknown artist who executed the Cloisters statue must have known and been influenced by Riemenschneider's profound characterizations. It is for this reason that the St. Roch appears to have been executed in the first decade of the fifteenth century, possibly in Franconia in the circle of Riemenschneider.

102 ST. MICHAEL?*

German, Lübruck, circle of Bernt Notke?, c.1490–1500
Wood, 33 in.
Lent by Michael Hall Fine Arts, Inc., New York

The remarkable statue of a saint in armor, presumably Saint Michael, is shown striding forward, straddling a *targe à bouche* shield, now broken. Dressed in a helmet with the visor up, a full-sleeved tunic, and richly ornamented armor, he appears to have been holding a spear in his right hand and possibly the scales with which to weigh men's souls in his left. Both these attributes have disappeared. An almost identical statue of St. George, which appeared on the London art market in 1966 (cf. *Connoisseur*, CLXII, May 1966, 54), was advertised as by Bernt Notke, about 1490. The close similarity of pose, armor, facial type, and size (the St. George was $32^1/2$ inches high) leaves no doubt that the two statues are by the same hand and leads one to conjecture that they may have been intended as a pair for some particular setting. But the resemblance of the two statues to the work of Bernt Notke is only general, and at best they could only be loosely connected with his circle.

It should be noted that both statues depart from the normal representations of their respective saints. Usually they are shown in the act of combatting dragons, but there is no evidence here either of the struggling or vanquished beasts or of the gesture of dealing a death blow with a sword or a lance, as for instance we find in the silver reliquary of St. George at Elblag attributed to Notke (Müller, 1966, pl. 139B). Even if the missing dragons were intended to be separate pieces, it would be difficult to reconcile the basically static, self-contained poses of these statues with violent combat. There is yet another anomaly. Normally both Saint George and Saint Michael were represented as youthful saints, and indeed both Notke's Elblag statuette and the large equestrian group of St. George in Stockholm depict them thus. But both wooden statues depict older men with mustaches. The possibility thus arises that neither statue is of a saint, but of a more contemporary personage. Because of the missing attributes and effaced shields, more positive identification of the figures will have to await the results of further research.

103   BOOK OF HOURS†

French, use of Rouen, circle of Jacquemart de Hesdin and the Bedford Master, c.1405–1410
Gold and tempera on vellum, 298 leaves, $8^1/_4$ x $5^1/_2$ in.
Text in Latin and French, 16 lines, 15 large miniatures
Lent by the Philadelphia Museum of Art ('45–65–5)
The Philip S. Collins Collection

The Book of Hours, a form of prayerbook used by the laity for private devotions, became increasingly popular by the end of the fourteenth century and was produced in staggering numbers throughout the fifteenth. Basically it consisted of a calendar giving the feast days of the saints normally celebrated in the particular diocese in which the owner lived (in this case, Rouen), a selection of lessons drawn from the four Gospels, two prayers dedicated to the Virgin, the Office of the Blessed Virgin divided into nine canonical hours to be read throughout the day, the Seven Penitential Psalms, the Office of the Dead, and private prayers and prayers to the saints. More elaborate Books of Hours introduced other series of Hours, such as the Hours of the Cross and the Hours of the Holy Ghost. The nature of the contents lent itself to illustration, normally to cycles depicting the scenes of the Nativity of Christ for the Hours of the Virgin, of the Passion for the Hours of the Cross, and of individual saints for the prayers. Equally important, Books of Hours were commissioned by private individuals—the members of the nobility, the upper mercantile classes, or the clergy—most of whom wanted to possess a resplendent object as well as the devotional text. It thus became the custom to preface each major section of the text with a miniature and to decorate the margins with elaborate borders.

The small Book of Hours from the Collins collection, probably executed for the lady who is depicted praying in a miniature on page 566 of the volume, is typical of this type of manuscript in France in the first decade of the fifteenth century. The miniatures have been attributed to artists under two different influences. The first artist, who executed the *Adoration of the Magi* (color plate), appears to have been trained in the circle of Jacquemart de Hesdin (Zigrosser, 1962, p. 19) and manifests close affinities with the style of the anonymous artist known as the Luçon Master (Meiss, 1956, p. 193, n. 23, and 1967, I, 357; see No. 104). Jacquemart was one of the artists employed by John, Duke of Berry, between 1384 and 1409. Some miniatures in the Duke's most important manuscripts (the *Petites Heures*, Paris, Bibliothèque Nationale, MS. lat. 18014; the *Très Belles Heures*, Brussels, Bibliothèque Royale, MS. 11060–61; and the *Grandes Heures*, Paris, B.N., MS. lat. 919) have been ascribed to him (Meiss, 1967, I, 169–176, 194–228). The second hand is an artisan who reflects the style of the Bedford Master, another anonymous illuminator active primarily between 1405 and 1430, who illustrated a Breviary (Paris, B.N., MS. lat. 17294) for the Duke of Bedford, the English regent who ruled France from 1425 to 1435 (see Spencer, 1965 and 1966).

The first style reflects an older tradition of placing the scene against a patterned background, here a myriad of red, blue, and gold squares. Yet the effect of the triangular floor tiles implies an awkward, intuitive attempt at perspective, and the staggered placement of the Magi and the enthroned Virgin suggests a growing interest in the representation of space. The Magi wear fanciful costumes typical of the first decade of the century, when the International Style in France reached its apogee in the art of the Limbourg brothers in the *Très Riches Heures* (Chantilly, Musée Condé, MS. 65) executed for John of Berry before 1416. The love of splendor manifested by this page is demonstrated by the visual *éclat* of the glowing yellows, reds, and greens and deep, luxurious blue of the Virgin's robe against the sparkling tessellated background. This same effect is carried over into the margins, where we observe that the heavy foliate branches of the fourteenth century (cf. Nos. 63–64) have now given way to a profusion of penned *rinceaux*, punctuated by stylized gold ivy leaves and burrs and occasional red and blue flowers. Thus miniature and text are enframed by a band of decoration that catches the light and reflects it in gleaming sparks. When one holds the book and turns the pages, the play of these reflections and the burst of brilliant colors give the effect of a jewel being examined.

More advanced trends can be observed in the miniatures by the second master. There is a greater interest in modeling the features and in indicating the volume of the figures, and props such as desks and thrones are used more effectively to suggest depth. An interesting development in a number of the margins, which are otherwise identical to that of the *Adoration of the Magi*, is the introduction of a multicolored acanthus sprig at the four corners of the heavy enframing *baguette*. Introduced from Italy in the early fifteenth century, this decorative motif occasionally competes with and then becomes assimilated with the typically French ivy-leaf decoration (see No. 106).

Former Collections: Spitzer Collection, Paris; Philip S. Collins.
Literature: Spitzer, 1892, V, 135, no. 3; Meiss, 1956, p. 193, n. 23; Bond, 1962, p. 471, no. 18; Zigrosser, 1962, pp. 18–19; Meiss, 1967, I, 359.

104 BOOK OF HOURS*

French, Ile-de-France, *c.*1405
Attributed to the Luçon Master
Tempera and gold on vellum, 20 miniatures
Text in Latin, 15 lines, 167 folios, $7^1/_8$ x $5^1/_8$ in.
Lent by the Walters Art Gallery, Baltimore (MS. W.231)

Attributed to an anonymous artist who is known as the Luçon Master for his illuminations of a Pontifical and Missal (Paris, Bibliothèque Nationale, MS. lat. 8886) for Etienne Loypeau, bishop of Luçon (1388–1407), the miniatures in this Book of Hours reveal the height of sensitivity and refinement achieved by the artists of the first decade of the fifteenth century around Paris. The illuminator's style is close to that of Jacquemart de Hesdin (see No. 103); in fact, the Luçon Master also illustrated a number of books that were in John of Berry's possession (Baltimore, 1962, p. 50).

The miniature of the *Death of the Virgin,* perhaps contemporary with or even slightly before that of the *Adoration of the Magi* (No. 103), is surrounded by a form of border decoration that prevailed at the beginning of the fifteenth century; heavier, painted *rinceaux* still punctuate the corners and midpoint of the outer margin. It should be noted, however, that in the evolution of these border forms, phases continually overlap each other, for this form of decoration also occurs in the *Belles Heures* of the Limbourg brothers (New York, the Cloisters), generally considered to date from 1410 to 1413. The miniature itself reflects the continuation of more archaic trends: the use of a tessellated background, a crowded and intuitively rendered space, and a restraint from the more boldly modeled, substantial forms that were beginning to manifest themselves in some manuscripts associated with Jacquemart's later career (e.g., the *Très Belles Heures,* Brussels, Bibliothèque Royale, MS. 11060–61, and the *Grandes Heures,* Paris, B.N., MS. lat. 919). Here the emphasis is on splendid decoration, on the sparkling, jewellike quality of the richly glowing colors. Lyrical and emotive qualities of line are combined to lend a new, gently sorrowful, psychological content to the deathbed scene. As the apostles crowd around, there seems to be the gentle murmur of prayers. Standing next to the bed is the figure of Christ, returned to earth for his mother's death. He holds an infant in his arms, the soul of the Virgin, which he will take back up to Heaven with him.

Former Collections: Roussin de Saint Nicholas, 1745 (erased); Benigne Charles Fleuret de Saint-Memin, 1750 (bookplate); Gruel.
Exhibitions: Baltimore, 1949, no. 84; Pittsburgh, 1951, no. 15; Los Angeles, 1953, no. 52; Baltimore, 1962, no. 47; Cleveland, 1967, no. VI–23.
Literature: de Ricci, 1935, I, 791, no. 214; Panofsky, 1953, I, 380, n. 48–4; Meiss, 1956, p. 193, n. 23; Meiss, 1967, I, 358, 394, n. 66.

105 BOOK OF HOURS*

French, use of Paris, c.1405–1415

Gold and tempera on vellum, 15 large miniatures, 24 small ones, $7^{7}/_{8}$ x 5 7/16 in.

Text in Latin, 228 folios, 13 lines

Lent by the Cornell University Library (MS. B.24)

Most of the fifteen half-page or full-page miniatures in this handsome book of hours from the Cornell University Library reflect the style of the ateliers of Jacquemart de Hesdin and the Luçon Master (see Nos. 103, 104). In the Cornell Hours, we find that the full-page miniature of the *Annunciation* (fol. 19v) is by a different hand from the fine historiated initial depicting the *Trinity* (fol. 20) and the marginal figures of musical angels on the opposite page. We also find that the borders of the two pages contain two different systems of ivy decoration. These differences indicate what inspection of the volume proves: the *Annunciation* is an inserted page. Further on in the volume, a miniature of the *Crucifixion* (fol. 141v) manifests an even greater departure from the usual decorative scheme, while a complete change of style and palette confirm the presence of still another illuminator. This page is also an insertion. The crude yet telling execution of the *Crucifixion* reflects the style of the so-called Pseudo-Jacquemart workshop as manifested in the Book of Hours in the Durrieu Collection (see Meiss, 1967, Vol. II, figs. 246–247), while that of the *Annunciation* appears to reflect the style of the Luçon Master and his workshop (Meiss, 1967, Vol. II, figs. 268, 486).

A more thorough presentation of the relationships between the miniaturists and their mode of decoration both in the Cornell Hours and in a more general context must await the results of further study. Suffice it to note for the moment that the *Annunciation* evinces a highly developed sensitivity to the rendition of figures as three-dimensional entities within a palpable space. This is accomplished chiefly by the black and yellow tiled floor, the darkening of the floor at the back as though it were receding into shadow, the effective modeling of the diaphanous draperies of the Angel and Virgin, and the striking contrast of their forms against the tessellated background. The whole scene is framed by a fanciful pink architectural framework.

Representations of the Trinity, as in the historiated initial opposite the *Annunciation,* gained considerable popularity at the end of the fourteenth century (cf. Mâle, 1949, pp. 140–144). Usually the figure of God supports either the Cross with the crucified Jesus upon it or the dead body of His Son. The rendition in the Cornell Hours is a happier and less emotional variant of this theme: the infant Jesus, who is holding the Cross almost as a plaything, is nestled in the arms of God. The Father holds an opened book in front of which hovers the Dove of the Holy Ghost. The intimacy and tenderness evident between Father and Son distinguish this as an unusual interpretation of the theme for the period.

Literature: de Ricci, 1937, II, 1233.

106 BOOK OF HOURS*

French, Paris, c.1420
Circle of the Boucicaut Master
Tempera and gold on vellum, 14 large miniatures
Text in Latin with some prayers in French, 151 folios, 16 lines, 6^1/$_2$ x 4^3/$_4$ in.
Lent by the Philadelphia Museum of Art ('45–65–12)

One of the most prolific ateliers of manuscript illumination during the second decade of the fifteenth century in France was that of the anonymous artist named the Boucicaut Master after his most famous production, the Hours of the Maréchal de Boucicaut (Paris, Musée Jacquemart-Andre, MS. 2: see Cleveland, 1967, no. VI–29). He and the Bedford Master (see No. 103) collaborated on a number of manuscripts, and at times their styles seem almost indistinguishable. The innovations that the Boucicaut Master made in the rendition of architectural space, landscape settings, and individual characterizations became, in the hands of his atelier and followers, a rather stylized, flattened, dry, and vacuous repetition of motifs and figure types. It was this latter style that dominated French illumination until after the middle of the century.

The artist of the Philadelphia Hours evinces a more distinctive personality than many of the workshop artisans who emulated the style of the Boucicaut Master; he also reflects many of the developments of the period 1410–1420. In the miniature of David Praying (fol. 73) that introduces the Seven Penitential Psalms, we find the King kneeling in an extensive landscape, which recedes from two conical rocks in the foreground across a wide expanse of greensward to the buff-colored hills in the distance. Although a naturalistic treatment of landscape in manuscript illumination may have begun as early as 1402 in the Très Belles Heures of John of Berry usually attributed to Jacquemart de Hesdin (Brussels, Bibliothèque Royale, MS. 11060–61, see Meiss, 1967, pp. 194–228; this attribution and date is still a matter of controversy), this miniature effectively demonstrates the more spatial, atmospheric treatment of an exterior setting that replaced the shallow shelf of grass and the patterned backdrops prevailing in earlier miniatures (see Nos. 103–105).

The border surrounding the miniature of David Praying consists entirely of scrolls of brightly colored acanthus leaves entwined around golden medallions filled with stylized flowers. In a number of manuscripts by the Boucicaut Master this form of decoration completely replaces the traditional French ivy rinceaux. Such is the case in one of the most spectacular manuscripts attributed to the Boucicaut and the Luçon Masters (Oxford, Bodleian Library, MS. Douce 144; see Oxford, 1966, no. 641), where it is evident that it is introduced in competition with, and sometimes even over, the normal ivy decoration. This manuscript is dated 1407, and there can be no doubt that the form and effect of its acanthus borders are derived from Italian manuscript illumination of the same period (see No. 109). This decoration was probably imported into France by such Italian illuminators as Zebo da Firenze, who introduced acanthus initials into the *Très Belles Heures* and employed borders analogous to the present example in a number of manuscripts he illuminated in Paris (e.g., the Hours of Charles the Noble in Cleveland, considered to date from 1400–1408; see Cleveland, 1967, no. VI–25, and Meiss, 1967, pp. 229–246, for bibliography and further information concerning this important personality). In the Philadelphia manuscript, as in most manuscripts of the fifteenth century, these elaborate, avant-garde borders decorate the principal pages of the book, while simpler, more traditional forms appear around the lesser miniatures and text pages.

Former Collections: Inscription: "Ce livre appartien à Gille Francois Mangan"; bookplate of Mantague George Knight of Chawton; Philip S. Collins Collection, no. 5.
Literature: Bond, 1962, p. 471, no. 16; Zigrosser, 1962, p. 22.

107 BOOK OF HOURS*

Northern French or Flemish (use of Rome), *c.*1440
Tempera and gold on vellum, 26 large miniatures
Text in Latin, 188 folios, 17 lines, 7⁷/₈ x 5¹/₂ in.
Lent by the Philadelphia Museum of Art ('45–65–4)

The miniatures of this handsomely illuminated Book of Hours manifest a greater assimilation of naturalism, both in the representation of pictorial space and in the acanthus borders. In the charming miniature of the Virgin nursing the Infant Jesus in the rose arbor (symbolic of Mary's purity—"a rose without thorns"), the curved and domical trellis provides a convincing spatial niche for the well-modeled, three-dimensional figure of the Madonna. In other miniatures of the book we find a well-developed but dry representation of a landscape in the *Annunciation to the Shepherds* (fol. 78v) and a still intuitively organized perspective rendering of the interior of a church in the *Mass of the Dead* (fol. 128v). The margins are replete with representations of figures relating to the theme of the main miniatures. Thus in the *Madonna in the Rose Garden*, five angels are picking the fruit that grows on the naturalistic plants around the page, a complement to the two angels offering bowls of fruit to the Virgin within the miniature. Likewise, peasant types cavort through the foliage around the *Annunciation to the Shepherds,* and five black-clad monks solemnly proceed around the *Mass of the Dead.*

This manuscript has been attributed to a Flemish workshop by Pächt and Nordenfalk, but Delaissé suggests a northern French origin, perhaps Amiens, about 1440 (Zigrosser, 1962, p. 27). The proliferation of marginal figures and the use of naturalistic border elements (perhaps ultimately derived from Italian sources and reflected in a Rouen workshop that produced a breviary completed in 1412, now in Baltimore, Walters Art Gallery, MS. W.300; see Baltimore,1962, no. 64) suggest an affinity with the late atelier of the Bedford Master. At the same time, the rugged modeling of the features of some of the figures and the tendency toward a more volumetric rendering of the bodies and draperies relate those miniatures to some in an incomplete Book of Hours in New York (Morgan Library, MS. M.358; see Pierpont Morgan Library, 1957, no. 32) possibly made in Luxembourg about 1430–1440. These associations with Rouen, the late Bedford atelier, and Luxembourg indicate that a northern French origin may be correct.

Former Collection: Philip S. Collins.
Exhibition: Grolier Club Exhibition of 1892.
Literature: Bond, 1962, p. 471, no. 22; Zigrosser, 1962, p. 27.

108 BOOK OF HOURS

Flemish, *c.*1500
Tempera and gold on vellum, 17 large and 22 small miniatures
Text in Latin and Flemish, 222 folios, 16 lines, 4 x 2³/₄ in.
Lent by the Walters Art Gallery, Baltimore (MS. W.428)

The pages of this small, elegantly illuminated Book of Hours exemplify the last phase in the development of manuscript illumination. There is no longer the concern for the purely decorative quality of the page in the surface patterns of contrasting ornamental letters and colored ground (see No. 23). Now miniatures are minute panel paintings with architectural and landscape settings, organized with increasing adherence to the laws of perspective. Space was thus created beyond the page and seen through a framed window that was the folio. This tendency to represent pictures on the page of a manuscript reached its highest expression in the fifteenth century (see No. 111). The striving for greater naturalism in the representation of things overflowed, as we have seen, into the borders (No. 107) and developed by the middle of the fifteenth century into some of the most extraordinary *trompe l'oeil* borders of the late Middle Ages in the Hours of Catherine of Cleves (see Plummer, 1966).

The final "subversion" took place when artists such as the Master of Mary of Burgundy (see Pächt, 1948) and the generation that followed him, as exemplified here, turned the whole page into an illusionistic painting upon which the text might appear as an inset piece of parchment not unlike a modern collage with a newspaper clipping. On the double-page spread commencing the Hours of the Virgin, this is precisely what has happened. The Virgin and Child are seen as though through a window cut into the page. The sill at the bottom, the shadows cast around the opening, and the firm modeling of the figures create the convincing impression of a niche. Around the window is a broad border against which plants and insects are illusionistically painted, casting shadows so that they appear to hover in front of the page. The text page presents an even more complicated spatial arrangement. Everything here seems to exist within the page as defined by the fine black line outlining the miniature. In order of recession, we enter past the beads, the foreshortened table-top, the arcading and colonnettes, and arrive at the shelves with the flower pot and the chalice above. The text panel occurs towards the rear; it is curiously tucked behind the left-hand colonnette of the arcading, but overlaps the two central ones, so that its surface corresponds to the outer edge of the shelf. Both miniatures are totally three-dimensional constructs in which surfaces that are parallel to the picture plane (or folio surface) are not what they seem to be: there are things in front of the left-hand folio if the border is the surface of the page and the text on the right is really part of the "picture."

Former Collections: Gruel and Engleman.
Literature: de Ricci, 1935, I, 877, no. 315.

109   GRADUAL†*
      Northern Italian, Lombardy, 2nd quarter of 15th century
      Tempera and gold on vellum, 12 large historiated initials, numerous smaller ones
      Text in Latin, 190 folios, $21^1/4$ x $15^5/8$ in.
      Lent by the Cornell University Library (MS. B.50++)

Virtually neglected since it became part of the collection of the Cornell University Library by the bequest of Andrew Dickson White, this spectacular Italian manuscript contains illuminations that are comparable in quality and *éclat* to the best surviving examples of their type. Large choir books of this sort were produced in great quantities in Italy in the late fourteenth and early fifteenth centuries; many have been cut up for their sumptuous initials, which are now dispersed in collections both in this country and abroad. Cornell is therefore expecially fortunate to have a book of this quality that is still more or less complete (only one initial has been removed).

The full exuberance of color and form can be discerned from the decoration of the Benedictus page (exhibited). Heavy, rich, swirling leaves of multicolored acanthus sprout from the initial B (*Benedicte domini* . . .), filling the upper margin, while a smaller foliate spray trails down the inner one. The initial itself is composed of architectural elements, a tall tower and a step-gabled house with a balcony supported on curving arms. A host of singing angels hover above gold and black clouds within the initial, adoring the figure of God, who appears in a flaming mandorla supported by a throng of blue angels. But the decorative impact and glowing colors of this illumination are rivaled by at least two other miniatures in the book. One, the *Ascension of the Virgin* (fol. 54; black and white illustration), contains a myriad of green angels swarming around a multicolored ringlet of cloud, while other angels, some assisting in the Ascension and others playing musical instruments, participate in the event. The richly embroidered gown of the Virgin, the emphasis on luxury and sumptuousness of color in this initial, equals the most elaborate examples of the International Style, the phase of Gothic that was evidenced all across Europe in the first couple of decades of the fifteenth century. The initial C depicting the martyrdom of St. Lawrence (fol. 51, color plate) is also composed of oddly bent architectural elements, but unlike the initials it contains a vestige of landscape with a fountain, an arcade, distant trees and hills, and a blue sky. Yet the extraordinary uses of color, as in the architecture and the king watching the torture, painted in "green monochrome," and the decorative qualities of the gold grid, the fruit-laden trees, the urns and peacock atop the arcade, all maintain the sense of splendor and fantasy of the International Style.

Although the manuscript is presently under study and will be published more fully in the near future, it is possible to indicate here that it belongs to a group of manuscripts produced in Lombardy and perhaps in the area of Milan during the second quarter of the fifteenth century. Several hands worked on the illumination of the Cornell Gradual, but the best artist, whose miniatures have concerned us here, is related in style with the artist of three pages from a Lombard Antiphonary that are now in Cleveland (Cleveland, 1963, nos. 71–73) and with another artist who executed three initials from a choir book attributed to the abbey of Monte Olivieto near Milan in the third decade of the fifteenth century that are now in the Pierpont Morgan Library (MS. M.558 A, B, and D; cf. Harrsen, 1953, no. 52, pl. 53). Our artist and the hands responsible for these other initials reflect in turn associations with the trend of northern Italian illumination from the highly elaborate style of Giovanni de' Grassi and Michelino da Besozzo at the beginning of the fifteenth century to that of Belbello da Pavia, who was active in Lombardy around 1430–1440. Certainly the Cornell initial of the *Martyrdom of St. Lawrence* comes close to emulating the style of landscape and architectural settings found in the latter's miniatures.

Literature: de Ricci, II, 1237 (cf. p. 1236).

110 PETRARCH, *TRIONFI, SONETA E CANZONI**
Italian, Florence?, *c.*1470
Tempera and gold on vellum, 2 historiated initials, 3 decorative borders
Text in Italian, 188 folios, $10^{1}/_{2}$ x $6^{5}/_{8}$ in.
Lent by the Cornell University Library (MS. Pet.+Z.12)

The fine illuminated introductory pages to the Triumphs, sonnets, and canzoni of Petrarch are no longer medieval in aspect. Script, introductory initial, and decorative border reflect a new Renaissance idiom, a format and style that the learned patrons of the fifteenth century considered to be approaching the forms of antiquity. Thus, a green wreath encircles a title inscription on the frontispiece, written in careful emulation of the epigraphic capitals found on Roman monuments. The text is no longer in the angular Gothic script, nor even in the *gotica rotunda* peculiar to Italy, but rather reflects the striving for a new clarity and regularity of form evident in fifteenth-century humanistic calligraphy. Historiated initials and foliate borders, borrowed from medieval traditions, are translated in a Renaissance style. In the first initial Petrarch is shown dreaming while Father Time retreats, and in the second Petrarch is shown wearing a laurel wreath and holding a copy of his work. Here, the antique author portrait has returned to its classical guise.

It is possible to identify numerous elements within the marginal ornament which derive from the medieval tradition. The interlace of white scrolled tendrils are a deliberate revival of early forms, such as those seen on the Beneventan page of about 1100 (No. 25). They are now organized according to a strict system, symmetrically disposed about the two gold bands of a supporting trellis and peopled with a profusion of Antique armorini, or putti. The arms of an unidentified Italian family, possibly those of the original owner, are incorporated into the decoration at the bottom of both introductory pages. Humanistic manuscripts containing similar three-quarter white vine borders and enwreathed title pages were produced in great quantities throughout Italy in the fifteenth century. In the Cornell Petrarch the particular choice of decorative elements, noticeably in the pendant and terminal arrangements, are closest to those considered to be of Florentine workmanship of about 1460–1470 (e.g. the Eusebius from the Corvinus Library, Hungarian Academy of Sciences, Cod. lat. 6: Berkovits, 1964, p. 122, pl. IV).

Former Collections: Ughelli, 17th century; Libri sale, 1859; Willard Fiske.
Literature: Fowler, 1916, p. 69; de Ricci, 1937, II, 1249.

111 FOLIO FROM A BOOK OF HOURS: CHRIST BEFORE PILATE*

French, Touraine, 3rd quarter of 15th century
Close to Jean Fouquet
Tempera and gold on vellum, $5^3/_8$ x 3 11/16 in.
Lent by the Lansburgh–Colorado College Collection, Colorado Springs

This miniature of *Christ before Pilate* reflects the infusion of a Renaissance style into French manuscript illumination. The miniature is conceived of as a panel painting, surrounded by an illusionistic frame simulating inset precious stones and pearls, while the bottom portion of the frame is given over to the text: "Deus in Adivtorivm mea intēde. . . ." The letters of the text are derived from, but do not exactly copy, the form of the epigraphic Roman capitals that Jean Fouquet first used in France in the monumental Hours of Etienne Chevalier now at Chantilly (Musée Condé: see Wescher, 1947, pls. 1–17). The medieval device of using letters of the alphabet as a decorative pattern against a textile background, as on the covering of Pilate's throne, has even been transformed from the angular Gothic to the clearer Roman capitals. Indeed the appearance of classical columns in the window and the creation of an ample space for the figures to move about in are largely due to the revolutionary impact of Fouquet, who appeared on the French scene about 1450 just after a trip to Italy and almost single-handedly introduced the style of the Italian Renaissance into France.

Although the distinctive format of the miniature and frame, which owes much to Jean Fouquet, should make it easy to identify other miniatures from what must have been a very handsome Book of Hours, it is problematical that it was executed by Fouquet himself. In the present miniature there is still an awkwardness of placing the throne according to the laws of perspective within the room, and there is a lack of that sense of volume in the treatment of the figures that we find throughout the Hours of Etienne Chevalier. The grainy, stippled brushwork is similar to the manner that Fouquet employs, but here the technique is coarser and more dominant than we would find in his miniatures. Moreover, there is an exaggeration of the features and a use of beady eyes that is not Fouquet's. However, one of Fouquet's followers, Jean Colombe, manifests many of these same characteristics, notably in the miniatures which he completed in 1485 in the *Très Riches Heures* now at Chantilly (e.g., the illustration for the month of November). While manifesting a debt to both artists, the illuminator of the present miniature may have been close to Fouquet in his Tours atelier.

112   FOLIO FROM A BOOK OF HOURS: KING DAVID*
       French, c.1500
       Circle of Jean Bourdichon
       Tempera and gold on vellum, 10 x 7 in.
       Lent by the Lansburgh–Colorado College Collection, Colorado Springs

The monumental dignity of this figure of King David, combined with a subtlety of modeling and a delicacy of palette, ranks this miniature with the finest works produced in the circle of Jean Bourdichon, the court painter to Louis XI and Charles VII at the end of the sixteenth century. The calmness and equanimity of the substantially rendered figure and the clear, gentle light of the landscape as it recedes to a golden horizon above blue hills bespeak of the balance, composure, and clarity of such contemporary Italian painters as Perugino. Indeed, the Hours of Ann of Brittany (Paris, Bibliothèque Nationale, MS. lat. 9474: see Mâle, 1946), which contains miniatures by Jean Bourdichon comparable with this illustration, can be seen as a collection of Renaissance paintings in which forms are clearly and simply stated, compositions are balanced, space is easily articulated, and the coloring is pure and lucid. This style was readily adopted by Bourdichon's contemporaries and became as standard a manner of painting in the late fifteenth and early sixteenth centuries as the style of the Boucicaut Master had become in the second quarter of the fifteenth century.

113 CHAINED BOOK
German, signed Frater Conradus Pater, dated 1476–1488
Vellum, original binding, chain
Lent by the Cornell University Library (MS. B.20)

This volume of religious tracts, signed and dated by a German monk during the third quarter of the fifteenth century, formed part of a so-called "chained library." It was frequently the practice in late medieval monastic, cathedral, and university libraries to attach books to their shelves by long chains so that they could be read on the sloping desk top below, but not removed from their location. As Streeter has pointed out in his study of the chained library, many early libraries employed this security measure (Streeter, 1931). This factor determined the shape of the combination book cases and desks, or "book presses," as they are called, and also the form of the medieval library itself, so that the presses could be placed near windows for light (p. xiii). Chains were still used at some of the college libraries at Oxford until the end of the eighteenth century (p. xiv). Seven such libraries have survived to the present day in England alone, among which the Cathedral Library at Hereford is the most renowned.

Literature: de Ricci, 1937, II, 1233.

114 TAPESTRY: WOODCUTTERS*
Flemish, Tournai, first quarter of 16th century
Wool, 10 ft. 6 in. x 11 ft. 3 in.
Lent by the Metropolitan Museum of Art (41.190.227)
Bequest of George Blumenthal, 1941

Woven tapestries of large dimensions were among the most sumptuous furnishings required by princely households during the Middle Ages. They were used as wall hangings, placed around the dank stone walls of the various apartments used by royal and noble families in castles which were heated only by large fireplaces. Such a tapestry, representing a battle scene, may be seen adorning the walls of the banqueting chamber of John of Berry in the miniature for January in the *Très Riches Heures* (cf. Panofsky, 1953, Vol. II, fig. 88). Tapestries were of course also woven for churches, where they served the same insulating and decorative functions. They were usually created in sets, as proved by numerous documentary references to payments for "une chambre de tapisseries" (see Soil, 1892, pp. 36, 240, 243). The numerous individual pieces needed to cover the walls of a large room in turn provided the opportunity for depicting many incidents from popular themes, usually secular for households and religious for chapels, churches, and cathedrals. Thus we have elaborate religious scenes of the Passion, incidents from the Old and New Testament, the visions of the Apocalypse. Secular cycles were derived from the legends of Alexander the Great, the romance of King Arthur, the representations of the Nine Heroes, the hunt, and scenes of courtly love set against a many-flowered, *mille-fleurs* background.

The tapestry from the Metropolitan Museum is representative of a genre of tapestry produced in the first half of the fifteenth century in which rustic or bucolic subjects abounded. The representation is ostensibly of woodcutters at work in an undulating, high-horizoned landscape dotted with distant towns and peopled by grazing deer, shepherds tending their flocks, and strolling nobles. As such, the tapestry falls into a set type, referred to by inventory and payment entries as "tapisseries à personnages de bucherons." Some "tapisseries de bosquaille et de verdure et partout . . . plusieurs grans personnages comme gens paysans et bocherons lesquels font manière de ouvrer et labourer audit bois par divers façons" were bought by Philippe le Bon from a Tournai tapestry maker, Pasquier Grenier, in April 1461 (Soil, 1892, p. 240). Similar sets were purchased in 1466 and 1505. The latter set was made for Philippe to be used en route to Spain, "pour fair mener avec lui et s'en servir en son voyage d'Espaigne" (pp. 36, 249–250).

In all cases, references to these particular representations imply that they were valued as scenes of rustic life. Thus they reflect a romantic attitude toward the pastoral life that one also finds in the Ambrogio Lorenzetti's Good Government frescoes in the Palazzo Pubblico in Siena, in the frescoes of the Torre d'Aquila of the late fourteenth century, and in the calendar miniatures of the *Très Riches Heures* by the Limbourg brothers. Warburg has noted that these tapestries of working peasants are in keeping with origins of northern realism and peasant humor found in Flemish paintings (Warburg, 1932, p. 229). Indeed there is a strong reflection of these elements in the miniatures and especially the marginalia found in fifteenth-century manuscripts (cf. No. 107), and both seem to lead naturally to the lusty genre paintings of peasants and tavern scenes found in seventeenth-century Dutch and Flemish art.

But neither the descriptions in the documents nor the assessment made by Warburg explain all the elements found in the woodcutters tapestry. We observe that the forest in which one of the peasants is working is encircled by a picket fence with a gate under an elaborate ogee arch. Numerous deer are grazing contentedly in the enclosed space, seemingly oblivious of the woodsman splitting a tree trunk. The shepherd in the upper left-hand corner appears to look upon the scene with bewilderment. The woodsman lopping the leaves off a branch in the foreground is flanked by richly dressed nobles, a lady holding a jar on the right and an aristocratic couple on the left.

The working peasants possibly connote the labors of the months or even the cycle of the seasons, for woodcutting was the labor commonly associated with the months of December or February as in the background of the February miniature of the *Très Riches Heures*. But the winter months must be precluded in the present tapestry because of the luxuriant foliage. Van Marle interprets such scenes as nobles making a tour of inspection of their serfs, a pictorial reminder not only of the distinctions that had to be maintained between the different classes but also of the benefits of good management of the estate (Van Marle, 1932, II, 57–61), in much the same manner as the Lorenzetti frescoes spell out the benefits of good government for both urban and rural society. Nobles supervise the cutting and stacking of logs in an early sixteenth-century tapestry in the Musée des Arts Decoratifs (Van Marle, 1932, Vol. II, fig. 430), while in the companion piece (fig. 429) the woodsmen are at work in the forest, surrounded by game. It would seem that the Metropolitan tapestry probably derives its form and basic meaning from these common representations, especially as it appears to have been one of four pastoral scenes of shepherds, grape harvesters, and peasants in the Blumenthal Collection. Yet there seems to be a deeper and more elusive meaning as well. The enclosed garden may be an evocation of the garden of paradise. Or it may refer to the Immaculate Conception of the Virgin, as in the *hortus conclusus* in which the Virgin was sometimes seated in fifteenth-century paintings (e.g., paintings in the Staedel Institute, Frankfurt, by a Middle Rhenish Master, or in the Museo di Castelvecchio, Verona, by Stefano da Zevio), and it may therefore, by extension, be a symbol of chastity. Perhaps this meaning is reinforced by the presence of the stags, symbols of purity and piety, here gathered around the tree of life (see No. 31). But if this is so, why are the woodsmen invading this paradise, and, equally strange, who is the Magdalene-like figure on the right with her ointment jar? Perhaps the answers to these intriguing questions can one day be resolved.

Former Collections: Count de Vauguyon, Paris; George and Florence Blumenthal, New York.
Literature: Bloch, 1926, Vol. IV, pls. VII, IX; Margerin, 1932, pp. 140–142.

Bibliography

Aachen, Suermondt Museum. *Mittelalterliche Kunst der Sammlung Kofler-Truniger, Luzern, Aachener Kunstblätter*, Vol. XXXI (1965).

Adams, Henry. *Mont-Saint-Michel and Chartres*. New York, 1933.

Alföldi, A. "Cornuti: A Teutonic Contingent in the Service of Constantine the Great and Its Decisive Role in the Battle of the Milvian Bridge," *Dumbarton Oaks Papers*, no. 13 (1959), pp. 171–179.

Athens. *Byzantine Art: An European Art*. (Ninth Exhibition of the Council of Europe.) Athens, 1964.

Baltimore, the Walters Art Gallery. *Early Christian and Byzantine Art: An Exhibition Held at the Baltimore Museum of Art, April 25–June 22, 1947*. Baltimore, 1947.

——. *Illuminated Books of the Middle Ages and Renaissance: An Exhibition Held at the Baltimore Museum of Art, January 27–March 13, 1949*. Baltimore, 1949.

——. *The International Style: The Arts in Europe around 1400*. Baltimore, 1962.

Barcelona and Santiago de Compostela. *L'art roman*. Barcelona and Santiago de Compostela, 1961.

Beckwith, John. *Coptic Sculpture 300–1300*. London, 1963.

——. *Early Medieval Art*. New York and London, 1964.

Beenken, H. *Bildhauer des Vierzehnten Jahrhunderts am Rhein und Schwaben*. Leipzig, 1927.

Beigbeder, O. "Le chateau d'amour dans l'ivoirerie et son symbolisme," *Gazette des Beaux Arts*, XXXVIII (1951), 65–76.

——. *Ivory*. New York, 1965.

Berkeley, University Art Gallery. *Pages from Medieval and Renaissance Illuminated Manuscripts from the Xth to the Early XVIth Centuries*. Berkeley, 1963.

Berkovits, Ilona. *Illuminated Manuscripts from the Library of Matthias Corvinus*. Tr. Susan Horn, Budapest, 1964.

Bier, J. *Sculptures of Tilman Riemenschneider*. Raleigh, N.C., 1962.

Binghamton, University Art Gallery. *Developments in the Early Renaissance*. Binghamton, N.Y., 1968.

Bloch, Stella Rubinstein. *Catalogue of the Collection of George and Florence Blumenthal*. Vols. I–IV. New York, 1926.

Boeckler, Albert. *Abendländische Miniaturen bis zum Ausgang der romanischen Zeit*. Berlin and Leipzig, 1930.

——. *Deutsche Buchmalerei vorgotischer Zeit*. Königstein-im-Taunus, 1953.

Bond, William H. *Supplement to the Census of Medieval and Renaissance Manuscripts in the United States and Canada*. New York, 1962.

Borchgrave d'Altena, J. de. "Notes pour servir à l'inventaire des oeuvres d'art du Brabant: Arrondissement de Bruxelles," *Annales de la Société Royale d'Archéologie de Bruxelles*, Vol. XLVII (1944/6) [1947].

——. *Notes-pour servir à l'étude des retables anversois.* Extract from *Bulletin des Musées Royaux d'Art et d'Histoire*, 1957–1958. Brussels, 1958.

——. "Statuettes malinoises," *Bulletin des Musées Royaux d'Art et d'Histoire*, ser. 4, XXXI (1959), 2–98.

Borenius, Tancred. *St. Thomas Becket in Art.* London, 1932.

Boston, Museum of Fine Arts. *Arts of the Middle Ages 1000–1400.* Cambridge, Mass., 1940.

Botkin, M. P. *Musée de l'Ermitage: Collection d'art Botkine.* St. Petersburg, Russia, 1911.

Bouvy, D. P. R. A. *Middeleeuwsche Beeldhouwkunst in de Noordelijke Nederlanden.* Amsterdam, 1957.

Brooklyn, Brooklyn Institute of Arts and Sciences, Museum. *Pagan and Christian Egypt.* New York, 1941.

Brummer, J. *The Notable Art Collection Belonging to the Estate of the Late Joseph Brummer*, Pt. I. Sale catalogue, Parke Bernet Galleries, New York, April 20–23, 1949. New York, 1949.

——. *Part Two of the Notable Collection Belonging to the Estate of the Late Joseph Brummer.* Sale catalogue, Parke Bernet Galleries, New York, May 11–14, 1949. New York, 1949.

Brussels, Musées Royaux d'Art et d'Histoire. *Art chrétien jusqu'à la fin du moyen âge.* Brussels, 1964.

Buddensieg, Tilman. "Central European Manuscripts: Ausstellung der Pierpont Morgan Library," *Kunstchronik*, XI (1958), 237–245.

Buffalo, Albright-Knox Gallery. *Religious Art.* Buffalo, 1964.

"A Gift of Romanesque Sculpture from the Spanish Government," *Bulletin of the Fogg Art Museum*, III, no. 2 (1934), 14–17.

Cahn, Walter. "Romanesque Sculpture in American Collections, I: Hartford," *Gesta*, VI (May 1967), 46–52.

Campbell, W. "A Romanesque Processional Cross," *Art Bulletin*, XXII (1930), 90–97.

Chapel Hill, William Hayes Ackland Memorial Art Center. *Medieval Art.* Chapel Hill, N.C., 1961.

——. *An Introduction to the Collection.* Chapel Hill, N.C., 1962.

Cheetham, Francis. *Medieval English Alabaster Carvings in the Castle Museum, Nottingham.* Nottingham, 1962.

Chicago, Art Institute. *Handbook to the Lucy Maud Buckingham Medieval Collection*, Meyric R. Rogers and Oswald Goetz. Chicago, 1945.

Chicago, Fine Arts Club. *Smith College Loan Exhibition.* Chicago, 1961.

Clark, K. W. *Greek New Testament Manuscripts.* Chicago, 1937.

Cleveland, Cleveland Museum of Art. *Gothic Art 1360–1440*, Cleveland, 1963.

——. "Twelve Masterpieces of Medieval and Renaissance Book Illumination: A Catalogue to the Exhibition, March 17–May 17, 1964," *Bulletin of the Cleveland Museum of Art*, LI (March 1964), 42–63.

——. *Treasures from Medieval France.* W. Wixom. Cleveland, 1967.

Coche de la Ferté, Etienne. *L'antiquité chrétienne au Musée du Louvre.* Paris, 1958.

Cologne, Kunsthalle. *Weltkunst aus Privatbesitz.* Cologne, 1968.